THE RISING PRICE OF LOVE

The Rising Price of Love

The True Cost of Sexual Freedom

Dr Patrick Dixon

Hodder & Stoughton

First published in Great Britain in 1995 by Hodder and Stoughton
A division of Hodder Headline PLC

10 9 8 7 6 5 4 3 2 1

British Library Cataloguing in Publication Data

ISBN 0 340 62772 7

Typeset by Hewer Text Composition Services, Edinburgh
Printed and bound in Great Britain by
Cox & Wyman Ltd, Reading, Berks.

Hodder and Stoughton Ltd,
A division of Hodder Headline PLC
338 Euston Road
London NW1 3BH

CONTENTS

ACKNOWLEDGEMENTS

First of all, I wish to thank the hundreds of people who over the years have been willing to share with me some of the happiness and pain of their lives. My hope is that we may all be able to learn through you.

In particular, I am very grateful to the following: Charing Cross Hospital Medical School Library for the kind use of their excellent facilities; Dave and Ann Carlos, who guided me to useful material; Nigel Williams and Dr Andrew Fergusson, for many helpful insights and comments; Chris Daykin, President of the Institute of Actuaries, for advice on some of the cost calculations; His Honour Judge Christopher Compston, for allowing me to join him in court; Chris Towner, for typing the first draft at such; Linda Crosby, for many patient hours of checking and editing the text; and James Catford at Hodder & Stoughton, who has been a constant source of encouragement and advice. I am also indebted to David and Gay Batten, for kindly making a flat available to write in for ten days.

Most of all, though, a big thank-you is due to Sheila, for 22 years of friendship and 16 wonderful years of marriage, and for her support, encouragement and advice in the writing of this book (as well as help in proof-reading); also, to our four children, John, Caroline, Elizabeth and Paul, for putting up with me being so preoccupied while the book was being completed.

Confidentiality

I have drawn from a rich tapestry of human experience as well as scientific research, and many have made themselves vulnerable in sharing the pain of their past. They have powerful stories to tell, although I have changed the details in order to keep their anonymity. So if you think you recognise someone you know in this book, then you are almost certainly mistaken!

INTRODUCTION

This book is about relationships between men and women, and the cost of sexual freedom: about what happens after a sexual relationship begins, the things we enjoy, and the price we often pay.

The lesson of history is that the pendulum is always moving when it comes to sex; it is still only for an instant at the two extremes of sexual abandon or strict moralism.

Many are now seeing the early stages of a new swing towards moralism, driven by concern over the cost of sexual freedom, and by the discovery of a broken generation of children who are now growing up with a deep hunger for something different.

This book is about that swing, and why it will be so significant. It is about the cost of a disastrous experiment that promised us liberty, but has left millions of people shattered and in chains. It is about a new social movement, a campaign for caution powered by worried parents and those who have suffered personally. It is about a new romanticism, a search for love in an increasingly fragmented age.

It is about the false media promise of the ultimate sexual experience, in a world where relationships are simple, and there are no babies or children involved. It is about impossible pressures to perform and conform; how people have been left feeling frustrated and dissatisfied, while increasing rape and sexual abuse are daily reminders to us that sexual freedom needs boundaries and self-control or it will surely destroy us.

It is about AIDS, reminding us that a partner with a

past can bring many hazards to health, including cancer and death. It is about a generation now desperate to have children, many of whom are childless because of infection during sexual relationships.

It is about men and women discovering that relationship break-up is rarely trivial, and often traumatic – with lifelong scars, emotional distress, poverty, loneliness and despair.

It is about a generation of children who have had to live through it all, a generation that is often destroyed psychologically as a result – affecting their schooling, self-image, health, sleep and behaviour, and making their own adult relationships more likely to break down; it is about many children leaving home, and turning to theft, vandalism or addiction.

It is about the cost to nations now measured in tens of billions for state benefits, health care, social support and fighting crime.

In view of all this, it is hardly surprising that many people are now asking if this form of sexual freedom was worth it, and their voices are getting louder every day. And all the while the clock is ticking away during the last years of the twentieth century to welcome in a new millennium, a world that will be built on new values, new understanding and new patterns of living.

We may debate the timing of the changes, the *exact* date of the new sexual revolution, but of its coming there can be no doubt. In some ways, this new revolution will be more traditional; in other ways, it will be very radical.

This book is about the new heterosexual culture beginning to dawn, and the urgent action that is now needed to help minimise the increasing human and financial costs of the old sexual revolution. If we don't heed these changes now, then we might see the pendulum swing to the opposite extreme: an authoritarian and repressive backlash.

First, though, we need to look back at the history of sexual relationships to put the new changes into context.

1

THE PENDULUM SWINGS AGAIN

Before we can make sense of the rapid reversals taking place in sexual relationships today, we need to look back on the last 300 years, and the three swings of the pendulum: from relaxation to restraint; and then back to relaxation; but now swinging back to restraint again. Only then can we look at what is happening right now, and make some careful predictions about the future. One thing is certain, though: there will be no re-run of the Victorian age. Although the pendulum is swinging back towards a new moralism, in the next century, a new millennium, it will be expressed in a unique way. However, we can still learn from the past.

In the early eighteenth century, sexual freedom was tolerated: sex was certainly on the agenda. Marriage in church was common, but it was not universal. Births outside marriage were growing, and that is why Lord Hardwicke introduced a Marriage Act in 1753 to regularise 'common law' marriages, with proper records to sort out problems of inheritance.

Then came a growing unease about the growing costs of sexual freedom as the effects of a massive spiritual awakening took a grip on the nation, starting with Wesley in the mid-eighteenth century, and crusading on throughout the nineteenth. Great reformers like William Wilberforce, who abolished slavery, or Lord Shaftesbury, who abolished child labour, were just part of a massive movement that championed change. This movement also affected the sexual climate. As thousands in every town and city discovered the Christian faith, a new moral code swept through Britain. However, not everyone necessarily kept to this code, hence the emergence of the hypocrisy, bigotry and double standards that we still detect today.

The restraint of the Victorians

Despite the double standards, many things did change profoundly. There was a new, widespread emphasis on sexual purity, restraint, virginity and personal duty, and this had an effect that lasted several generations; the same thing may be about to happen again.

At its extreme, this new code produced such strict modesty that watching someone swimming 100 years ago might be seen as a perverted act. A society woman had to cover most of her body before slipping into the sea from the front of a bathing machine – a hut on huge wheels that was pushed out into the water from the beach.

However, the Victorians certainly had sex lives, and often we have a warped view of them that is not backed by the facts. Michael Mason has written in *The Making of Victorian Sexuality* that widespread sexual repression in the Victorian era is a myth,[1] with between a third and a half of women pregnant at marriage, middle-class couples kissing and cuddling in public, and 'unbridled sexual intercourse' taking place in working-class dance halls. Another study of one Dorset village discovered that eight out of ten births were illegitimate between 1870 and 1890. There is no evidence that this was typical of the whole country, but it does suggest that our view of all Victorians as morally strict is incorrect.[2] Mason also claims that the Victorians were fully aware of female sexuality. Dr William Acton's famous quote – that most women are 'not troubled by sexual feeling of any kind' – was actually written to help young men afraid of impotence. Victorian doctors certainly knew about female orgasm, as seen in their writings and teaching.[3]

While the *extremes* of Victorian prudery may be a myth, there is no doubting that times were certainly very different then when compared to today. Divorce only became legal after the 1857 Matrimonial Causes Act, and by 1914 there were still only 856 divorces a year. Eighty years later, in 1994, the figure was 158,700.[4]

The swing against Victorian values

Just as the Victorians reacted against the previous century's sexual abandonment with a radical sexual revolution of their own, almost as soon as the nineteenth century ended, another reaction and revolution followed – one that has continued to swing more or less without interruption towards the sexual freedom that we see today.

The First World War, 1914–18, helped drive a new sexual culture into the heart of the nation at a time of revolution in Europe. Radical new ideas emerged in the 1920s about relationships, women in the workplace, votes for women, of clothing, short hair, short skirts, skimpy necklines. The divorce rate shot up as soldiers returned from the war, and then stabilised at twice the previous level.

In the early 1940s, sexual relations were still relatively 'prim and proper', despite increasing numbers of 'war babies'. Keith Waterhouse has written that it was 'extraordinarily difficult to lose one's virginity' at this time.[5] He also wrote: 'Girls went in terror of becoming pregnant – as did boys of impregnating them.' Condoms were available, but were not usually carried on a date. 'Convention very strongly laid down that respectable girls didn't do it until they were married, or at least properly engaged . . . and the government had mounted a fearsome campaign against VD that made today's onslaught against AIDS look like a warning against tooth decay.'[6]

Another sexual revolution follows the war

After the end of the Second World War a floodgate of sexual liberation was observed in many countries; a recent comprehensive sex survey shows that behaviour in Britain began to change dramatically in the mid-1950s, not – as is often thought – following the advent of the Pill, which happened a decade later.[7] However, the Pill may have had an accelerating effect.

In 1967, William Masters and Virginia Johnson influenced a generation with their book entitled *The Sexual Response*, which described what happens to men and women during sex. More recently, they have said of the 1960s and 1970s: 'There was a rush to make sex recreational, to make it fun and games, and ignoring the things that make sexual responses occur, things that deepen a relationship, that give it colour and endurance.'[8]

In 1969 the Divorce Reform Act was passed, and by 1981 one in nine marriages lasted less than six years, compared to 1 in 80 in 1951.[9] The 1970s and 1980s were two decades increasingly obsessed by new sexual freedom. In fact, it could be said of the early 1990s that never has there been a time when so many have been so publicly preoccupied for so long about their next orgasm, or someone else's. This trend could be seen on the television – in love scenes, on chat shows, comedy acts, documentaries, song lyrics, pop videos, and, of course, the all-pervading adverts.

The *New York Times* said recently:

Virtually every magazine on the newsstand, every book in the drugstore, half the stories in the tabloid press, vast quantities of television entertainment and movies galore, depict sexual philandering as a common and casual pastime. The result can only be that any monogamous folks wandering this cultural Sodom and Gomorrah feel positively freakish. Yet let some high-profile politician be caught at the deed, or even be accused of it, and public shock suggests that adultery is the most unheard of thing America has ever heard of.[10]

Sex today

One reason for this inconsistency is that the pendulum of private behaviour has not swung quite as far as the media image. People may be having lots of sexual relationships, but usually only one at a time, and far fewer than you may think. In reality this sexual revolution has changed us less than some suggest – this is just as well, for the changes that *have* happened have been enough to wreck a generation.

So much, then, for the last 200 years, and the revolution in sexual relationships over the last 40 years, but what is happening today? Despite the popular image of free love and the desire for a better sex life, 40 years after the so-called sexual revolution began, most people still want to be faithful. The American National AIDS Behaviour Survey of 11,000 people in 1993 showed that 90 per cent of heterosexuals are monogamous, and only 10 per cent have two or more partners in a year.[11] Half of all British women say a married person having sex with someone else is *always* wrong, and it was six out of ten in 1983. For men, the 1993 figure is four out of ten.[12] Then we need to add a larger number who say it is *usually* wrong to have an affair when married. Therefore, most people are more restrained today than perhaps we thought.

But what sexual revolution are we talking about anyway? White heterosexual Western values? Gay values?

Ethnic minority values? Values in the developing countries that make up most of the world? The problem
is that national surveys tend to merge distinct groups
together into an average, and the smaller sex surveys
in multicultural countries like the United Kingdom also
ignore huge differences *between* ethnic groups. For example, Asian communities have always had a strongly
traditional, ethical code on sex, while Afro-Caribbean
communities are often more tolerant of single parenting.

Countries like India or China have their own sexual
history,[13] but something else is now happening in white-
dominated heterosexual Western culture.

A cry for change
In the mid-1990s, there are many signs of change. As
history has demonstrated, sexual fashions are part of
social change as a whole, and they are interwoven in
a dense fabric of cultural influence. A growing unease
concerning who we are and what we have become is
beginning to spill over to new thoughts about sex; and
in Britain and the United States, cries from the heart
have been expressed after a series of atrocities; some of
these were sex-related, others not, but all contributed to
the unease.

One such shocking event in the United Kingdom was
the abduction and murder of two-year-old James Bulger
in 1993 by two ten-year-old boys, who led him crying
and bleeding through the streets before killing him. They
knocked him unconscious with heavy stones and then laid
him in the path of an oncoming train. Why did they do
it? Was there a sexual element in the attack? Why did
no adult stop them? There was suddenly a huge surge of
feeling throughout the country that something was very
wrong with our society if we could allow such things to
happen.

Can we really go on like this? What kind of world are we creating? Slowly, we are realising that we cannot go on in the same pleasure-dominated direction. *My* pleasure may be *your* nightmare. *My* right to do what *I* like may be *your* loss of freedom or life. *My* search for love with your partner may wreck *your* chances of love. This gradual rejection of the 'pleasure principle' is changing how we want to bring up our children, and altering our relationships and lifestyles – in other words, challenging life after sex.

'Back to Basics'?

A new age is now dawning, with a new code for living as radical as anything that has changed us before. In Britain, the Conservatives' 'Back to Basics' slogan soared into orbit: it was a symbol of post-Thatcherism identity crisis and malaise; a post-imperialist, post-unionist, post-individualist, depressed Britain on the eve of a new era, a new revolution in the making.

Many, like Lord Rees-Mogg in *The Great Reckoning*,[14] have tried to predict global trends for the next century. Sexual change is part of these trends. An indication of the new thinking is the way sex education is changing in schools as a result of parental pressure. Parents of today's teenagers are a group aged between 35 and 55, and many are reaching the top echelons of influence and power. So what are their opinions about sex?

If we believe those who say that the permissive sexual revolution is alive and well, fully on course to go into orbit into the next century, jettisoning the family unit, heterosexual marriage, long-term ties and the chain of reproductive processes, we may be in for a big shock. If we are on course for more of the same, then we would expect the parents of today's teenagers to be driving that philosophy forward. These parents were born between

1940 and 1960, and were teenagers in 1955–75 when very dramatic changes in sexual expectations took place. They have first-hand experience of the sexual revolution, and their reactions today are very significant. Are we heading for more of the same? Should we wind the clock back? Should there be something new?

It has been said by some of those who lived as young adults in the 1960s era that there was generally more talk of sex than *actual* sex, and we have yet to experience even a fraction of the original 1960s dream of free love, community living, group parenting or trial marriages. Even Dr Masters said recently, at the age of 78, 'Sometimes it feels as though nothing has changed. In spite of all the incredible availability of sex-related material, I feel we're back where we started.'[15]

However, we all agree that society had a taster of sexual freedom. So what is the verdict? What do today's parents say now? What do they want for their own children?

Parents are worried about sex

These parents are worried; they say we have gone too far already, and are deeply conservative when it comes to their own children. As part of my AIDS work, I have gone into schools, met pupils, talked to teachers, spoken to governors, and met hundreds of parents. My experience and that of others suggests that there is now a clear consensus among parents: many are anxious that their own children might want to follow the lifestyle dreams, aspirations and behaviour that they experienced at the same age. They are worried about copycat behaviour, and have a recurring nightmare that their own teenage daughters or sons might go further than they did.

These parents are 'clock-watchers' – many wishing they

could turn back the hands of time to restore expectations of long-term faithfulness and commitment, and the principle of waiting for as long as you can for the right person to come along.

Part of this concern is because of AIDS. Since the British AIDS campaigns started in 1987, there has been a big debate about putting the message across. What is the most effective way to prevent AIDS? People laughed at pictures of icebergs. However, the laughter turned to anger in schools as the message changed to a high-profile, safer-sex condom campaign.

The message was generally felt to be right for an adult national campaign – but for pre-puberty 12-year-old girls?

The United States is embarrassed by the condom culture

In the United States, the condom campaign was far more sensitive – even for adults – and yet there has been an even stronger reaction in schools. The government only dared launch a national adult campaign promoting condom use in 1994, 13 years after the first AIDS cases, when over 600,000 were already infected with HIV.

However, within a week, one advert had been withdrawn, and questions were being asked about the remainder. The campaign was a series of television and radio advertisements aimed at 18–25-year-olds. The banned advert was for alternative rock radio stations, and seemed to show Anthony Kiedis, lead singer of Red Hot Chili Peppers, taking his clothes off and putting on a condom.[16] All four major television networks agreed to take the other advertisement, but felt nervous – restricting them to late-night slots only. The press gave huge coverage to the views of conservative Congressmen, and to Evangelical and Catholic church officials who said the campaign would backfire by promoting sex.[17]

The point I am making is that older adults on both sides of the Atlantic are much more cautious and conservative about sex than might be thought; and the pendulum never swung as far in the first place as the media hype has suggested. As it begins a swing back, it does so from a place already more restrained than some would like. But how far will this new swing of the pendulum take us?

Erotic condoms – but adults still hate them

In Britain, a public health condom message was more acceptable, but 'experts' said that this was not enough. Surveys showed that many people hated condoms: they were difficult to put on, slippery, unreliable, leaked, burst, split, fell off, interrupted lovemaking, smelt horrible, and producing one implied a lack of trust or worries about the past; and on top of all this, when it was all over, disposal was messy. Hardly an erotic turn-on for a night of passion.

So the experts had an idea: sell erotica as part of the 'condom experience'. In other words, show erotic images at the same time as condoms, and everyone will be halfway to orgasm at the very thought of queuing up to buy them.

However, the experts forgot one important thing. Erotica might possibly sell condoms to adults, but it would never do in the classroom because the parents of today's teenagers are wanting to change future sexual history. They are hoping they can alter the way their children will live, away from how things were when they were young, and away from 'condomania'. These parents are hanging on to the pendulum with all the might they can muster, hoping to drag it back to a middle position.

'Condom sex' flops at the school gates

In many countries, parents have an important role in shaping what children are taught about sex in school, and in Britain this was formalised by Parliament in the 1980s. Such rights tend to get exercised. This resulted in materials from the Health Education Authority costing millions being blocked at the school gates because parents and governors were sick of experts trying to give their children a one-dimensional message to use condoms, without any reference to relationships, commitment and family. These parents were fed up with the 'Thought Police'.

Many parents were also very concerned about crude, explicit or 'lewd' lessons on sex by adults 'who should know better'. Hence there was a national outcry in March 1994 after Leeds pupils aged 10 and 11 had 'Mars bar parties' (using chocolate bars during oral sex) explained to them in response to a question. There were also protests over role play involving 'Mummy', 'Daddy' and 'Mummy's lover'.[18] This lesson was given by a nurse visiting from the Health Authority.[19] One mother said: 'When I heard about the lesson on affairs I was very upset, but my child was almost too embarrassed to talk to me about the lesson involving Mars bars.'

If the sexual revolution is still very much alive, supported by those who grew up in it, wouldn't this mother have welcomed a relaxed and uninhibited approach, giving children an education free from sexual repression, fears and guilt, teaching teenagers to have wonderful, creative orgasms? The mother disagreed: 'We are not prudes. My son knows how babies are made, but he does not need to know about perverted sex.'[20] Her views were echoed at the time by a great many others.

Two days later, the headteacher of another school apologised after 10- and 11-year-olds arrived home from school using graphic terms for sexual intercourse and other acts, following one sex education class taken by someone outside.[21]

Parents against the 'Thought Police'

Here is yet another sign that change is coming. Recently, I helped conduct a national survey of some of the estimated 60 per cent of British schools that requested a radically different sex education booklet to those currently available. (I wrote this booklet myself, with help from others.) This was part of my work in helping to develop an independent national AIDS prevention programme for schools.

Who decided what was taught about sex or AIDS, and where and how? Teachers were given several boxes to tick: education authority, headteacher, head of year, governors, parents, others. Out of the approximately 250 schools that replied, almost all ticked more than one category – but none ticked the education authority. The 'Thought Police' had lost and parents had won.

The booklet drew on the experience of a team of educators from the AIDS organisation I started in 1988,[22] who visited the schools. They had already seen several thousand pupils face to face, and opinions were gathered from pupils, teachers, governors and parents.

The approach taken was the one insisted on by almost all the adults concerned. (Pupils themselves might have liked explicit erotica – we would never have been allowed that option, so we did not ask their preference on this.) The adults agreed they wanted clear facts, attractive presentation, lifestyle options (including a positive view of postponing sexual activity), long-term monogamy, choices, self-respect, and being able to resist peer pressure.

So who got it right? The official, expert-backed condom approach, or a more restrained stance that mentioned celibacy and monogamy as possibilities to consider?

History speaks for itself

We launched an initial 100,000 colour booklets in the House of Lords in December 1991. Although greeted with derision and contempt by some 'experts', the booklets were a runaway success – with overwhelming demand from teachers. In fact, the entire print-run disappeared within a few weeks. A further 250,000 booklets were hastily reprinted, and that stock lasted a further year.

Something was happening. Take-up was rapid in government schools, special schools, privately funded schools – mainly for 14–16-year-olds. Over 10,000 teacher packs and 3,500 demonstration videos went out. Almost overnight, it became the most widely used literature resource on sex and AIDS in British schools.

The survey showed that almost every school found the booklets useful and wanted more. Many who were originally using them for just a class of 30 now wanted copies for a whole year. Some ordering previously for a year group now wanted enough for the entire school.

Parents confront the 'Thought Police'

The demand for the booklets was massive and rapidly growing. Teachers talked to teachers, governors to governors, and parents to parents. While some education authorities placed bulk orders, one individual in one authority decided that the materials were so awful that they wrote to every school and other education authorities, warning them about the 'moralistic' content. Yet schools continued to order the booklets in ever-increasing numbers – since when were they going to let the 'Thought Police' tell them what to do?

A new booklet was produced in December 1993. It had better illustrations, a larger format, an updated expanded text, new cartoons with scenarios showing peer pressure and how to resist it – and the same options of abstention and monogamy listed among others. Some 250,000 of these booklets were printed, intended to last a year, but all went in just 16 weeks – quite a remarkable fact considering there are only about 600,000 pupils in each school year.

The booklets were also used in prisons, hospitals, clinics, colleges, youth clubs and churches. Some were requested by other nations: Canada, Australia, the United States, New Zealand, South Africa and many others, and they were also translated into Romanian and Czech. Perhaps culture was changing elsewhere too. The vast majority of booklets went to British pupils, though, and eight out of ten took their copies home to keep. And still the demand grew.

Sex 'experts' wiped out as 'irrelevant'

Educators from the same AIDS organisation had also personally taken classes attended by over 150,000 pupils. Seven out of ten schools polled said they wanted a personal visit from the same organisation, with the same message.

So what had happened to the permissive 'sex culture'? The answer is that the world has begun to move on and has left these sex education 'experts' behind. Stuck in a mid-1970s psychological rut of promoting the old sexual revolution to teenagers, the so-called experts have been wiped out as an irrelevance.

Consumerism is having its day, and consumers who themselves were products of the sexual revolution are now voting overwhelmingly for something new: not for prudery, repression or double standards, but for sexually fulfilled, long-term, happy relationships full of pleasure but free from disease and the fear of AIDS. The last thing they want is some trendy youth worker teaching girls how to achieve orgasm or telling boys how to roll condoms on to bananas.

Politicians follow the crowd

The British government has also begun to follow the crowd, with stronger statements about the need for a clear moral framework in sex education, and arguing that it had always been a part of policy. Headlines depicted the Education Secretary in a 'moral crusade', while the Health Minister stepped in to ban a 'smutty' health guide.[23] It was written in 1994 by Nick Fisher, 'agony uncle' of the magazine called *Just Seventeen*; it was funded by the Health Education Authority to be sold in bookshops. All 15,000 copies were pulped,[24] but another publisher soon snapped it up.[25]

Was this to be the end of the Health Education Authority's out-of-date sex education role, after bitter rows and a ban on further sex-education materials pending a review?[26] The government was plunged into further controversy some four weeks later when a junior Health Minister said condoms could be given to 12-year-old girls if it was the only way to protect them from pregnancy; this was an option that many parents found disturbing, especially if contraceptives were being handed out to their daughters without their consent.[27] Labour opposition speeches also began to change, with Tony Blair and others stressing an emphasis on the family.

Then came a new video resource for schools called *Make Love Last*, produced by Care Trust; this had a more up-beat message about 'waiting for sex' than anything seen before. Launched on 14 February 1994, around 1,500 schools ordered copies in the first four months 'to show teenagers that saying no to premature sex is a positive and rewarding choice'.[28]

So are we moving from a political to a moral agenda?

Possibly so, but perhaps sex behaviour is neither political
nor moral at root, but relational: an act of desire between
two people. Therefore the changing pattern of relationships is the one thing most likely to have the greatest effect
on the sexual revolution to come.

The US 'say-no' campaigns grow

Major changes in sexual culture are also taking place in
the United States; indeed, the swing back of the pendulum
began there. While sexual culture has generally been
more relaxed in the United States, sex education there
has paradoxically always seemed shockingly traditional
to those in Europe. Now, though, there are new parent
protest movements sweeping across the United States,
with even stronger 'say-no' campaigns than in Britain.
In fact, such movements would be rejected outright
in Britain as ultra-moralistic, although the Care video
is breaking new ground. These new US groups have
created sharp controversy in an increasingly polarised
society.

In February 1994 there was a big reaction in southern
California to a new Christian sex education programme
urging abstinence.[29] The 'Sex Respect' campaign, as it
was called, visited Acacia Middle School near San Diego.
Pupils aged 12 and 13 were given T-shirts with printed
slogans on them, such as 'Stop at the Lips', and badges
saying 'I'm Worth Waiting For'. Pupils were reported as
chanting 'Be Confident, Be a Virgin', or 'Do the Right
Thing, Wait for a Ring', or 'Don't be a Louse, Wait for
a Spouse'.[30]

Driven by the same kind of parent pressure as has
been seen in Britain (though with a far more explicit
moral message), the programme has grown fast, with
some 1,600 schools taking it up, together with schools
in 24 other nations.[31]

Parents who object to encouraging abstinence

When fashions and trends change, some people always need time to catch up. In Acacia, one parent withdrew her child from the school in protest at the new culture promoting abstinence, and is planning to take court action if 'Sex Respect' is not dropped from the syllabus.[32]

Yet the programme is based on more than fashion, for it does seem to be effective. In 1991, researchers at the Psychology Department of Brigham University in Utah looked at three different sex education programmes encouraging abstinence in seventh-, eighth-, ninth- and tenth-grade students across three school districts. The 'Sex Respect' programme produced the highest scores for reported attitude changes, although converting that into proof of behaviour change is more difficult.[33]

Parents in the United States are particularly worried for several reasons: first, they have an even higher teenage pregnancy rate than Britain (and Britain has one of the highest in Europe). Although parents argue that this is a reason *not* to encourage yet more teenagers to have sex, many sex education 'experts' see these high pregnancy rates as the strongest argument in their favour for explicit sex education promoting condoms.

I remember leading a local youth group in Washington DC in the mid-1970s where it seemed that sexual activity in the 13–16-year-olds was about ten years ahead of what was happening in the United Kingdom (this was confirmed by later surveys). So perhaps it is not surprising that the United States has felt the costs earlier and begun to react sooner. People there have also been far harder hit by AIDS than any other developed country. The United States is seeing more people die of AIDS every year than died in the entire ten-year Vietnam War.[34] They are trying to build a post-AIDS world while some countries are still pretending that AIDS does not exist.

Many pupils now say 'true love can wait'

On 29 July 1993, up to half-a-million signed cards pledging abstinence and monogamy were placed in the ground on Capitol Hill by the 'True Love Waits' campaign. Each signed card said: 'Believing that "true love waits", I make a commitment to God, myself, my family and those I date, my future mate, and my future children to be sexually pure until the day I enter a covenant marriage relationship'.[35]

Marie Claire magazine describes 'a new sexual revolution sweeping America . . . the biggest shift of social behaviour since the free-love movement of the 1960s'. The campaign was started in 1992 by Southern Baptist minister Richard Ross, who has become an instant success as a TV chat-show personality, and the movement has been empowered by the explosive spread of an enthusiastic Christian faith in young people.[36] Those noting the new moralism in the United States may point to alarming or encouraging signs, depending on their stance. There is certainly a new hunger for something to fill what is widely felt to be a moral vacuum – even if people cannot agree on what it should be.

The same vacuum is felt in Britain too, hence the launch of 'You, Me, Us!' by Citizenship Foundation and the Home Office in Britain in 1994 to try to help young children tell the difference between right and wrong;[37] and there is now a consensus among all the major political parties that young people need to be taught social values for the health of our nation.

So, then, we have seen that widespread culture changes are already beginning, with more still to come, powered by anxious parents and, in the United States, by increasingly influential Christian groups.

The truth about sex

I want to return for a moment to sexual behaviour today, because there is a lot of confusion, and it is affecting how we feel about the future. There seems to be a lot less sexual activity taking place than you may have thought, although surveys on sex can be seen almost every week in some magazine or another. After years of raunchy headlines, convincing us that the whole world is 'doing it', the truth is beginning to dawn: the pollsters have conned us.

Popular polls done over the phone or conducted in the street are not a reliable way to find out about sex. In fact, British confidence in opinion polls sank drastically in the wake of an unexpected Conservative victory at the 1992 general election. And if polls on politics are problematic, then polls on sex are simply perilous. Many such surveys are flawed before they start, because some publications only sample their own readers. In contrast, the surveys used as research evidence in this book are ones properly designed with representative samples of sufficient size.

Many sex polls are useless

The exact wording of a question in a survey can influence the answer. Take, for example, the issue of masturbation, which is a guilt-inducing subject for many people. If you pose the question 'When did you *last* masturbate?' instead of 'Have you ever masturbated?', then you will get very different responses. We also have to ask how a particular survey was conducted. Intimate face-to-face interviews of men by women may get different answers than if the interviewers are men – or the other way round. Likewise, age, ethnic origin, perceived differences in background between interviewer and interviewee, or other factors can also affect results.

Perhaps these are some of the reasons why the most comprehensive sex survey ever conducted in Britain of

19,000 people, published in 1994,[38] drew so many different conclusions to the famous surveys published by Kinsey in the United States in 1948 and 1953.[39] We have been told over and over again that Kinsey found at least one in ten of all males to be homosexually active. However, the UK national survey discovered that only 1.7 per cent of men reported a male sexual relationship in the last five years, ranging from 5 per cent in London to only 1 per cent for the rest of the country. This result was dismissed by some, but painstaking care was taken in the survey methods, and similar studies published almost simultaneously in France, Canada, Norway, Denmark and the United States found almost exactly the same results – between 1 per cent and 4 per cent. The US survey was of 3,321 men aged between 20 and 39, carried out by the Batelle Human Affairs Research Centers in Seattle, Washington. The aim was to see how many were at risk of HIV.[40] Only 1 per cent of men reported sex with other males only over the previous ten years, although another recent study in 1994 by the University of Chicago gave slightly higher figures.

Kinsey's sampling was poor

The 10 per cent figure from Kinsey in 1948 seems to have acquired the status of 'Absolute Truth'.[41] However, even when you add figures from the new studies of men who have had sex with both men and women over the previous decade, the figure still only adds up to 2.3 per cent.

Kinsey's sample was flawed, for one in four of those interviewed were former or current prisoners; a high proportion of these were sex offenders, and he recruited many others from his lecture classes. To be fair to Kinsey, his claims were often distorted by others. For example, he only claimed that 10 per cent of men between 16 and 55 were more or less exclusively homosexual in activity for up to three years.

Some gay-rights groups feel that in a hostile climate

and with insensitive questions, the recent surveys are also likely to be misleading. We have to accept that when it comes to finding out about sex, people may not want to tell us – and even if they agree to be interviewed, they may not tell the truth.

There is much less sex than men claim

What about heterosexual relationships? Is the picture of what people do today flawed as well? Almost all sex surveys discover that men report lots more partners than women, so who are all the women? The women deny it's them! Researchers say that the difference is explained by male bravado and female bashfulness. Yet distorted results from previous surveys can put huge pressure on people to 'follow a crowd' that doesn't in reality exist. For example, because survey after survey has suggested that half of all British teenagers are sexually active by their sixteenth birthday, tens of thousands of self-respecting 17-year-olds have felt that in order to be normal, they probably need to join in and 'do it' as well. Thus there is the danger that such surveys result in a false self-fulfilling prophecy.

These amateurish or wrongly reported sex surveys have also affected the debate about how explicit sex education should be and when it should start. If a quarter are sexually active at 14, then perhaps explicit sex education is needed at 11? Many of these unscientific sex polls have been wrong. The much larger British National Survey of Sexual Attitudes and Lifestyles, carried out during 1990 and 1991, found that only 18.7 per cent of 16–19-year-old women reported first intercourse before their sixteenth birthday, and 27.6 per cent of men.[42] A different survey found rates as high as 40 per cent, but the interviewers only talked to those already having sex – so the result was distorted.

All of these recent results are generalisations; they

hide, for example, the less than 1 per cent of Pakistani, Bangladeshi and Indian women reporting first sex before 16 years of age.[43] Those with a Christian faith were also less likely to be sexually active before the age of 16, with the exception of Roman Catholics, who were slightly more likely than the general population to be sexually experienced.[44] This might be because some teenagers can react against a strong moral line. Also, the Catholic Church has a large nominal membership: many people who say they are Catholics have values and beliefs more typical of those without faith.

Three-quarters of new students are virgins

Education and background also affect age of first sexual experience. You might think that students are most likely to have lots of partners in a liberated age, but the opposite is true. Men going on to higher education in Britain are on average three years behind the sexual experience of those friends at school who leave at 16 with no qualifications, while the figure for women is two years.[45] Three out of four students starting college in 1994 had never had sex before. Even fewer had a regular sexual partner, or had had sex with someone in the last year.[46] These discoveries are a big shock to students when they start talking to each other. Before they turn up on the first day, the great majority must be thinking that as virgins they may be in danger of being labelled as part of a prudish minority, while the truth is that they are in the vast majority. I was talking to a medical student in her third year of training just the other day. She said: 'We are all very conservative. I was really surprised. Conservative in every way, especially when it comes to relationships. Not what I expected from what you read.'

However, it may not be education or intelligence that discourages early sexual activity; instead, it may be cultural expectations and values. Whatever the reasons, the fact is that it seems that only a quarter of British A-level students are sexually active at age 18.

The teenage magazine message that 'everyone is doing it' is dangerous, life-threatening, and emotionally destructive nonsense,[47] because, as we will see, early sexual activity harms many teenagers emotionally and damages their health – even killing increasing numbers many years later.

So, then, the great pendulum of sexual culture is swinging slowly towards a new conservatism, as radical a change as any we have seen over the last 300 years; and it is swinging back from a far less extreme position than we thought, judging by recent scientific studies of sexual behaviour, which all show how much more restrained we are than the images would suggest.

If that is the case, where will we end up? Will the swing be slight – or will it take us to a strict puritanism? The answer will be found by looking at key areas where the sexual revolution has let us down: the need to feel loved, the abuse of sexual power, sexual illness, the emotional cost of break-up and divorce, damage to children, and the huge costs of paying for all this. But first I want to look at our need to be loved and the search for love – both made harder rather than easier over the last four decades.

2

THE SEARCH FOR LOVE

One of the reasons why monogamy is still so popular is that the revolution in sexual relationships has done nothing to help the fundamental human search for love; indeed, it has actually made finding secure love far more difficult in a fractured world. It is important for us to understand this need, because it lies at the very heart of the changes we are beginning to see today. The stark fact is that having several sexual partners a year does little to fill the empty void – it often leaves it even emptier than it was before.

Unlike sex drive – which is temporary, erratic, affected by age, circumstances and illness – the need to be loved is an instinctive desire in every person, as every psychologist will testify. This need to be valued, affirmed, cared for and understood starts on the day we are born and remains with us until we die. It is therefore a more constant drive than sex alone, yet often becomes muddled with it. This search for love can drive some people to have many sexual partners, but it drives a far greater number of us to have *few* sexual partners – and is the force behind monogamy.

When sex can destroy long-term love

In contrast, teenagers looking for love often do have sex as a result. In fact, surveys demonstrate that it is one of the commonest reasons they give for having sex;[1] they hope that sex will make love last.[2] Unfortunately, experience often proves to be the opposite, for one way to make long-term love *less* likely can be to have a sexual relationship before marriage – and the quickest way to destroy the relationship completely is to have sex with someone else when you are already married.

Loss of virginity, or a 'one-night stand', is one thing, but what is the effect of a longer-term sexual relationship outside marriage?

Cohabitation is one kind of sexual relationship that has been studied intensively. Cohabitation is widespread – almost one in five couples aged between 16 and 59 were unmarried and living together in the United Kingdom in 1992.[3] However, those couples who cohabit before marriage are also 50 per cent more likely to divorce after five years, and 60 per cent more likely to be divorced after ten years, compared to those who wait until marriage before living together[4] – that's a very big risk. When you have enjoyed some of the rewards of marriage without the cost of commitment, marriage after cohabiting is almost certainly likely to feel less special. A honeymoon becomes an anticlimax – if it happens at all – and everything else just carries on as before. So much for sex leading to lasting love – the reality is that sex outside of marriage can wreck a marriage. Of course, the search for love is particularly acute after the loss of a relationship, and this perhaps explains why those separated, divorced or widowed are twice as likely as those single or cohabiting to have two or more sexual partners each year.[5]

So what do people dream when it comes to sex? If we can answer that, we will know what they want for their lives. The answer is that there are two different dreams: one driven by pleasure, the other by the search for love.

The sexual revolution tells us that people's dreams should be of free sex, wandering from one relationship to another; probably enjoying a full sex life by the age of 16; feeling free in adultery without guilt or disapproval from others; seeing lifetime commitment as unrealistic and boring. However, the reality of our dreams is a little different. The dreams are confused, and we can listen in to them through the media, which is market led and provides images, sounds and words that people are willing to spend time and money consuming.

Torn between two fantasies

The images show that we are torn between two fantasies. The first, particularly for men, is exhilarating, boundless, endless sex in as many exciting situations as possible with lots of different people. This is the fantasy of pornography. The second fantasy is that an amazing person walks into your life, you fall in love with him or her, and have a passionate, beautiful, fulfilling, exciting, life-changing, perfect relationship that goes on and on for ever. This is the fantasy of the romantic ideal.

Between the two can be the dull reality of a neglected relationship that is no longer fulfilling nor exciting. But surely there must be something better? So which of the two fantasies will survive the conflict? Romantic love or sensation-seeking? Which of them will drive tomorrow's generation the most?

Attempts have recently been made by the entertainment industry to fuse the two fantasies together: sex pleasure and romantic love. In the film *The Getaway*, released in 1994, screen co-stars Kim Basinger and Alec Baldwin performed some of the most explicit sex scenes since Basinger appeared in the film $9^1/2$ *Weeks*. Yet in a clear demonstration of the changing culture, the co-stars exploited the fact that in real life they are married, to help allay public doubts about sex on the screen.[6] At a time when the US film industry is facing legislation to curb sex and violence, Basinger and Baldwin became the leading ambassadors of 'hot monogamy', a new formula for a post-AIDS world, combining elements of safe sex, eroticism and family values. Other recent monogamy-oriented films include *Far and Away* (Tom Cruise and his wife Nicole Kidman), *Flesh and Bone* (Dennis Quaid and his wife Meg Ryan) and *Love Affair* (Warren Beatty and his wife Annette Bening).[7]

Romance is big business

Romance is a powerful force, and the last five decades or more have been filled by millions of romantic dreams. Romance is undoubtedly a money-spinner – look at Mills & Boon, who publish new titles on romance every couple of weeks. Barbara Cartland is said to finish writing a new romantic book every month to satisfy the almost insatiable demand by the female audience who like to dream.

Literature has fed off romance for hundreds of years, and romantic heroes have sometimes died for it. As Annabel Heseltine recently wrote in *The Sunday Times*:

> Sex is wonderful. Without romance, though, it is like vanilla ice cream without chocolate sauce – nice but not delicious. Without romance there would be no surf on the waves, no fire in the volcano and the champagne would be flat . . . Those everyday experiences – whose turn it is to do the washing up or change the nappies, her face packs and nanny problems, his fag ends and whisky-tainted friends – hardly make for exciting literature or deep pillow talk.[8]

In the opinion of Dr Masters, it may be true that women are more romantically inclined than men: 'Men usually have affairs to find sexual variety and excitement, while women are more apt to have affairs looking for emotional returns. To put it another way, men have affairs seeking genital strokes, women have affairs to get ego strokes.'[9]

Finding the ideal partner

Romance is the driving force behind partner selection and hopes for a lasting relationship. As I write this, in front of me is an advertisement for a book called *How to Find Your Ideal Partner*, aimed at the millions each year who scan personal-ads columns or lonely-heart sections. This book promises to 'reveal how single people of all ages can find an ideal partner for a loving permanent relationship'.[10]

Then there are dating agencies – hundreds of them across Europe, Australia and the United States. Dateline is the world's largest computerised database, matching tens of thousands of people every year. It has an advertising budget of £2.5 million and a membership of over 35,000 of the 13 million single people in Britain between the ages of 16 and 60.[11] Dateline succeeds with slogans like 'Finding your Perfect Partner'.[12]

Or if you are already in a relationship, you could always rate its future chances with a special questionnaire used by 750,000 couples throughout the world, designed in the 1960s by David Olson; this questionnaire is used by Relate and other marriage organisations.[13] The 'marriage and partnership' charity, One Plus One, has also produced a questionnaire for engaged couples, in order to help them assess their compatibility.[14]

We can also see the romantic ideals in the marriage statistics, for the number of marriages in Britain is the second highest in Europe.[15] The vast majority of those getting married are optimistic about their relationship – and their goal is to be happily married for many years to come. This should be more or less self-evident – otherwise, what is the point of all the expense and bother, not to mention possible legal or financial hassle in the future?

Perhaps this dream of lasting marriage is why three times as many adults in the United Kingdom said in 1993 that divorce should be made more *difficult* as those saying it should be made easier.[16]

Most marriages still last a lifetime

Romance has protected the institution of marriage from rapid destruction. In 1927, the *Chicago Tribune* ran an article that predicted marriage would be 'Kaput' in 50 years.[17] There is not much sign of that today in the United States or anywhere else: in 1984, it was predicted that 96 per cent of those born in the United States in the 1930s would be married at some point in their lives.[18] The figure today is still 90 per cent.

Despite the divorce figures, the fact is that most marriages in the United Kingdom *do* last a lifetime, although this may not be true of those marrying today. Lifelong commitment can and does work – and it will not do to dismiss the majority in long-term marriages as unhappy but trapped. I have seen the long-term happiness and mutual fulfilment of marriage more vividly than most, through looking after those who are dying. Time after time, I have seen retired people preparing to lose husbands or wives through cancer, utterly devastated by bereavement after 20, 30, 40 or more years of happy life together. Of course, I have also seen many people who have reached the end of their lives as single people, and happy to be so, with years of warm memories and achievements they look back on.

Undoubtedly, the commonest sexual pattern is monogamy. For example, someone might say: 'This is the one relationship I believe in. I am not sure how long it will last, but it could last a lifetime, and because the relationship is important to me I am not going to chuck it all away by risking an affair or a one-night stand.' In fact, just ten minutes of infidelity can destroy a relationship, let alone a whole night. One 1993 British survey of women found that two-thirds would not forgive a single act of infidelity by their partners. Therefore the quickest and easiest way to wreck a relationship is to have sex with someone else – just once will suffice in most cases.[19] Men are slightly more tolerant of unfaithfulness – just over half would forgive one act of infidelity, but three out of four would walk out if it happened again.[20]

There are huge differences between men and women, though, when it comes to relationships generally. For example, if it came to a conflict between job and relationship, only 6 per cent of women would put the job first, and almost six out of ten would choose the relationship as the priority.[21] The percentage of men putting job before relationship is far higher.

Looking for unspoilt goods

The conflict between romance and pleasure-seeking can mean double standards. One friend of mine taught school lessons in Germany on sex and AIDS. At first the class said they all wanted to have many different partners; then they were asked what they were hoping for later on in life. Many said that they expected to get married. They were then asked which they would prefer: to get married to someone who had had many partners, or to someone who had had none? The class thought for a while, caught between the search for pleasure and the search for love. In the end, both sexes decided that while they wanted to enjoy a lot of sexual experience now, they were hoping very much to eventually marry someone with very few previous partners – if any at all.

This double-think is common: 'Have a good time now', yet 'Everything must feel very special when I get married'. At its extreme, we see the double-think in the case of women who are paying cosmetic surgeons large sums to repair their hymens so that they will feel like virgins again.[22]

Jane Alexander writes in *New Woman*:

So you're proud to be a mature, sexually experienced woman? Watch out. Celibacy and saving yourself for Mr Right are the new guidelines for Nineties sexuality. Women embarking on new relationships are now making a bid to regain their lost innocence – with the help of a cosmetic surgeon's knife . . .

In the Seventies and Eighties virginity was a nuisance, a frontier to be crossed to move from adolescence to womanhood . . . But now sex is an altogether different ball-game. Whether it's the all-too-real threat of AIDS or the fashionable interest in 'Back to Basics' family values, the new morality is everywhere. Suddenly it's cool to be celibate. Women can announce they are saving themselves without being laughed out of the bedroom.[23]

People may need to choose: do you want to invest all future sexuality in a 'big' relationship with long-life appeal, or scatter your experiences around? The reality is that one may exclude the other.

The pairing instinct is strong – *and* good for you

The sexual revolution never managed to alter the basic pairing instinct, and this is still a driving force. For both sexes, this instinct is powerful: as Desmond Morris reminds us, it is basic to the social conditioning of many mammals.[24] Pairing begins to happen at an early age – in fact, one study of 29,000 11–16-year-olds at the

University of Exeter found that nine out of ten teenagers said they had had a steady boyfriend or girlfriend by the age of 16.[25]

With a continued emphasis on the romantic dream of a perfect long-term relationship, the recent public trauma over the separation of the Prince and Princess of Wales is more understandable. They were our models: the hope of many for their own lives became focused on these two fallible human beings, who quaked under the strain of so many people living out their romantic fantasies through them.

We all like to believe that the romantic dream is possible – and we go on believing. Just around the corner could be the right man or woman for me, or for my friend – and that is one of the pulls towards infidelity and divorce: the ever-present hope of the *perfect* life beyond the current relationship. Thus high divorce rates themselves can be a product of an unrealistic romantic idealism. The very hopes we have for a better future may only serve to destroy a stable partnership, leaving us with nothing.

We want love because love makes us feel good about ourselves – and that feeling also contributes to our physical health. More and more medical research is showing that secure love is good for us, as well as being enjoyable. This should hardly come as a surprise, since the effects of a lack of love are all too obvious to anyone who cares for people – doctors, social workers, health visitors, teachers and pastors will all testify to this. Studies show that people in stable relationships stay healthier both physically and emotionally, with greater resilience to stress and change than if they are on their own.[26] Divorced or separated people are four times as likely to need psychiatric help, while single people are twice as likely to need it.[27] Married people also tend to adjust to illness or disability better.[28] All this adds fuel to the fire that is consuming the old values that have tended to poke fun at permanent relationships – claiming they are boring, old-fashioned or worse.

Married people live longer

Married people live longer too. The average risk of dying each year is lower if you are married, and the effect is even greater for men than women.[29] One national US survey in the late 1980s of 6,484 people suggests that one reason for this could be that many spouses 'monitor and attempt to control their spouse's health behaviours'[30] – encouraging them to go for health checks, take medication, lose weight, do exercise, cut back on alcohol, etc. Women are more likely to take responsibility for their spouse's health than vice versa, though.[31]

A Scottish study in 1992 gave a different explanation for the 'health benefit' of marriage.[32] The researchers wanted to find out how marriage kept so many of the 1,042 55-year-olds in their sample healthy; the evidence suggested that better material resources, lower stress levels, and how supported people felt, could all affect health.[33]

Remarriage can also be good for health – especially if the marriage is happy and decision-making is shared. The fewer children there are involved in the new household, the healthier a remarried woman will tend to be – and most of all when all the children at home are her own.[34]

Not all researchers have found all these benefits, though. For example, one study of 21- and 24-year-olds found no link between marriage and emotional or physical well-being, so perhaps it takes some years for such effects to show.[35]

So, then, we have seen that the dream of lifelong happiness with a faithful partner is still very much alive – and, if anything, is becoming stronger; as it does so, the pressures against the old sexual revolution continue to grow. Long-term relationships become even more important the older you get, and our population is steadily getting older as people live longer and birth rates fall.

Older people are gaining in numbers and influence

So much of the 1960s to 1990s sexual culture has just been a culture of the young, yet there is more to adulthood than the aspirations of those in their twenties – and older people today are certainly making their presence felt. They also are a force for change; they have sex lives too, and values that are more restrained. Those of retirement age have always been more conservative, while – as we have seen – the next age level down are altering their views as they live long enough to count the costs of the old sexual revolution.

There is a lack of youth in many developed nations. Europe has the lowest birth rate of its entire history – only 1.48 children per woman in a lifetime. At the same time, there is a big bulge of 55–70-year-old men and women with fewer dependants, yet with time, money and influence.

Five years ago, a company wanting to sell vacuum cleaners on television would show a young and glamorous woman – and one who was *not* wearing a wedding ring. If there was a man in the advertisement, he would be portrayed as her live-in partner. The woman in the advertisements today is more likely to be in her fifties, married, with a husband portrayed as a 'new man' – retired, at home, sharing household duties, enjoying a renewed lease of life together, because that is now the image most likely to sell to this new market.

Our advertising culture is simply a collection of images it invents for itself, and this is a dramatic change of image as the companies fall over themselves to court this growing market of mature people. The cult of youth is likely to fade over the next two decades, replaced by a growing recognition of the value of wisdom, experience and a certain 'gravitas' that comes only with the years.[36] This will profoundly affect sexual culture, as we have seen happening with sex education policy in schools. Older parents also have strong views on the media, feeling that it can be an unhelpful influence.

Older people have their own needs

Neugarten writes of those in the middle years: 'They are the norm-bearers and the decision-makers, and they live in a society which, while it may be orientated towards youth, is controlled by the middle aged.'[37] They are often looking for help in marriage at a time when pressures are easing, children have grown up, and their lifestyle is becoming more comfortable.[38]

Agony columns have yet to catch up. They are still full of 'My boyfriend is 25 and I am 17, should I have sex with him?' or 'My girlfriend says if I won't marry her, she's going to leave me for another man'. Such agony columns are likely to be replaced by columns in new-style upmarket magazines, with such questions as 'My wife has severe arthritis of the hips, but we have an active sex life – what positions do you recommend?' or 'My husband had a coronary three weeks ago after having sex – I'm afraid to touch him, but we both want to have sex again.'

There is a whole new world out there of middle- to later-years couples who are not interested in the latest adolescent titillations – they may have been enjoying orgasms for years, and perhaps are far more expert than many of the young agony aunts themselves. What they want is advice on keeping marriage happy, and sex life fulfilling. Agony great-aunts, here we come! Such people want to know how to enjoy sex if you suffer from angina or arthritis, asthma, bronchitis, diabetes, epilepsy, hernias, hormone deficiency, hypertension, kidney failure, multiple sclerosis, obesity, prolapse, prostatectomy, psychiatric illness, stroke, thyroid problems or urinary tract infections – to name but a few of the relevant health issues.[39]

Older sex therapists point the way

The advice of sex therapists Masters and Johnson is 'ageing' too, changing with the years to target older people. Virginia Johnson was asked what happens if you are married and no longer want to have sex – is it possible to have a healthy, happy and contented marriage without it? She replied, 'Sure! Why should any experts be the arbiters . . . That's like telling someone they can't be a vegetarian.'[40]

Therefore the ageing population is another pressure point as a new era dawns where people want lifelong romantic happiness, rejecting the view that it is unrealistic. Many people have older friends for whom this ideal is a living, daily reality, and there are many 'success' stories in the media reinforcing the idea that lifelong happiness is possible. At the same time, older people have always been more aware of the power of sex to destroy: the plague of sexual ill health, the pain of parting, the devastation of splitting up, and the problems for the children left behind.

So, then, we have seen that the pendulum is swinging yet again: sexual culture is changing, driven by many things, including the search for romantic love. I now want to look at the so-called freedom promised by the old sexual revolution, and how it has led to abuse of sexual power, as well as impossible pressures; we will then see how both these things are likely to make sexual restraint seem more and more attractive.

3

FALSE FREEDOM

The sexual revolution promised us sexual freedom and new-style liberated relationships, but that freedom has turned out to be a false promise because of the way it is being misused by some to dominate and oppress. This new freedom has also put many people under tremendous new pressures and has left many confused about how to conduct sexual relationships.

First, let us look at the abuse of sexual power. Over the last few years, concern has been growing about this whole area. We might hope that wherever freedom grows, so does a sense of responsibility, but the power of uncontrolled sexuality can be terrifying, bringing the supposed merits of sexual freedom into doubt. I hardly need to describe how sex can control and drive a man or woman as powerfully as any drug. The sex act itself releases pleasure-inducing chemicals in the brain, so there we have the basis for a true chemical addiction.

Yet B.F. Skinner, the famous behavioural psychologist, showed how people can be conditioned, just like animals, to respond to pleasure and pain.[1] If the extremes are great enough, so the theory goes, behaviour can be controlled completely. Therefore the pleasure we get from sex can encourage us to behave in all kinds of ways.

Sexual arousal can be a factor in people losing control, for sex drive can alter perceptions. When a man or woman is near the peak of excitement, they can behave in ways they later find deeply embarrassing – for example, two colleagues getting carried away after a party at work, and making love in an office where they are likely to be discovered, or a woman who cries out during orgasm somewhere where she could be overheard, or a couple taking part in a sexual act that some might consider perverted – and that even they might find hard to explain to themselves in the cool light of day. Thus sexual drive is powerful, and a celebration of sexual freedom tends to remove commonly accepted boundaries for permissible behaviour. But where does that lead us?

Danger raises sexual tension

Danger can also heighten arousal. Dr Estela Weldon of the Portman Clinic in London pointed out recently, after the death of a British MP during an act of auto-erotic asphyxia, that for some, 'risk is part of the pleasure, risk is part of the excitement'.[2] This is one reason why some people enjoy having affairs, or enjoy having sex in public places.

Part of the challenge of maintaining a long-term vibrant sexual relationship may be reintroducing a sense of danger, of the unexpected, of the outrageous, or the indulgent – making love in a field, a provocative dress, a weekend of passion in a hotel, making love in the Mediterranean sea by the light of the moon, or on a deserted beach at dusk.

Any sexologist could list a hundred examples of things people do at the height of passion that they may be unable to reconcile with their own self-image. Every week, the law courts or tabloids reveal more of the 'double life' of sex. In the dock is a quiet man who is regarded as a loner by his friends. He has never been known to be violent, yet he savagely strangled a 12-year-old girl after subjecting her to terrible sexual abuse. Or the respectable man arrested after repeatedly dropping his trousers outside a nurses' home.

Power games are part of many sexual relationships: at its most innocent level, there are the friendly struggles for dominance that are entirely verbal, or the playful fight that ends in laughter for both partners. At the other extreme, there are well-known patterns of battering and being battered – or even worse. Some people tend to place themselves in so-called 'classic' relationships, where they are likely to slip into familiar roles of battering or being battered, sexually abused – or possibly even raped. What started out as increasing sexual freedom can become a nightmare of sexual tyranny and domination: freedom for some people, but oppression for others.

Rape and 'date rape' – or is all rape the same?

The whole debate over sexual power has soared to new heights of controversy and confusion with publicity about 'date rape'. Some streams of feminism, described by Naomi Wolfe (*Fighting Fire with Fire*) and Katie Roiphe (*The Morning After*), are beginning to create a culture where normal, informal dating may soon become impossible.

The date rape debate is having a growing impact on changing attitudes to sexual behaviour in the United States. To understand why, we need to look first at the horrific reality of violent rape. It has always been there, but is more common today. Then there is the recognition that not all rape involves violence: there are other, more subtle, ways that men use to force a woman to have sex.

In the United Kingdom, there was great debate over the Angus Diggle case in 1994 – a young solicitor jailed for three years after attempting to have sex with a woman he had invited back to his flat for the night. He claimed he was innocent and had merely misread the signs. He was convicted for attempted rape, upheld on appeal – though with a reduced sentence.[3]

Together with this trend is a growing understanding that just because a woman has agreed to marriage, the ceremony itself does not give automatic consent in advance for sex whenever and wherever the husband demands it. However, this area is still confused in law, with a recent British case of a man cleared of raping his wife two days after she said yes.[4]

Then there was the case of Lorena Bobbitt in the United States, who accused John, her husband, of marital rape after being charged herself for assaulting him with a knife, amputating his penis. She was acquitted, and so was he – her acquittal was seen as just, and his acquittal as wrong, by almost six out of ten women in a *CNN/USA Today* survey.[5] Her acquittal led to strong reactions from the 10,000-strong US National Organization for Men, and the 32,000-member Male Liberation Foundation – both seen as extreme groups by the Women's Action Alliance.[6] These cases are all part of the changing picture; but before we can fully understand the date rape debate, there is another important question to be examined when it comes to accusations of rape.

How do you prove rape – or innocence?

How does a woman prove rape if there is *no* evidence afterwards of violence and *no* other witness to the act? And how does a man prove innocence if falsely accused? To some, such a suggestion arouses terrible anger, but on what basis can we safely conclude that all women are absolutely perfect and only men are evil? Some men may rape, but all human beings can sometimes be tempted to exaggerate or lie, especially if unhappy in a relationship.

Sorting out what has actually happened can be very difficult where children or teenagers are involved. In the

British press, there has been a great deal of publicity about teachers accused of sex crimes they have not committed, and whose whole careers have been wrecked as a result of a chance remark by a pupil. The National Association of Schoolmasters/Union of Women Teachers says that around 600 teachers a year are falsely accused – a trebling since the 1989 Children's Act.[7]

One teacher was taken from his home in handcuffs after three girls claimed he indecently assaulted them in front of a class. The charges were dropped – there were 24 other girls who witnessed the entire lesson – but not before he lost his job.[8]

The union's annual conference called on pupils to be expelled if allegations arc later found to be false, urging the union to pay for defending these cases in court. Yet the threat of expulsion could make genuinely abused children terrified to speak up.[9]

What do you mean by 'rape'?

The vast majority of children, teenagers or adults who claim to be victims of rape have indeed been raped – that is, physically overwhelmed by a man who has sex with them by force. Rape is a terrible crime, damaging an increasing number of women for life. And men too – for male rape is not unusual.

However, the really big question is how far do you stretch the definition of 'rape'? The *Oxford English Dictionary* definition is 'forcible or fraudulent sexual intercourse, especially imposed on a woman',[10] but is that enough? The 'date rape' movement has gone far further in a new definition of rape, and in doing so has unleashed new forces, such as the 'Take Back the Night' movement, that are helping to kill off the sexual revolution by rewriting the unwritten rules for behaviour between men and women.[11]

'Date rape' became a household phrase in the United States almost overnight after *Ms* magazine published the first results of a study on rape in US universities by Dr Mary Koss, claiming that one in four college women were victims of rape or attempted rape;[12] and in the same month the *New York Times* published an article on the same theme.[13] Date rape was now a reality, but what was Dr Koss's definition?

The female students were asked if they had ever gone out with a man who had put pressure on them to have sex. Pressure might have been verbal or chemical (plying a woman with alcohol or drugs) – and not necessarily physical. However, 73 per cent of those labelled by Dr Koss as having been raped did *not* say they thought they had been, and 43 per cent of the 'date raped' went on to have sex voluntarily with the same men afterwards.[14]

Pressure is abuse of power

Pressure means abuse of power to have sex, and abuse of power means sexual abuse, and sexual abuse means rape. That is the line taken by some. But how much of courtship involves subtle pressure? Could the whole process of courtship, as we have known it, become outmoded?

At the most extreme end, there are a few feminists who take the line (or appear to in the media) that all sex can be rape and all men are rapists. Andrea Dworkin, for example, says 'seduction is often difficult to distinguish from rape. In seduction, the rapist bothers to buy a bottle of wine.' She is also an aggressive campaigner against pornography. Her book *Intercourse*, published in 1987, suggests that sex is an act of male oppression to subjugate women.[15] Gloria Steinem, author of *Outrageous Acts and Everyday Rebellions* and *Revolution from Within*, said, 'a woman needs a man like a fish needs a bicycle'; and Germaine Greer, author of *The Female Eunuch*, wrote: 'women fail to understand how much men hate them'.[16]

This strong line by very influential feminists implies to other feminists a basic hostility not only to men in general, but also perhaps to heterosexual women who may have a sexual appetite for more.[17] Katie Roiphe describes vividly the increasing confusion in many young American single men, who are now unsure how to behave. She also describes a new culture, very different from a few years ago:

In this era of Just Say No and No Means No, we don't have many words for embracing experience. Now instead of liberation and libido, the emphasis is on trauma and disease. Now the idea of random encounters, of joyful, loveless sex, raises eyebrows. The possibility of adventure is clouded by the spectre of illness. It's a difficult backdrop for conducting one's youth . . . The sexual revolution hasn't been entirely erased by a new ethos of sexual conservatism . . . Everywhere we look there are signs of sexual puritanism, but there are also signs of sexual abandon . . . the shift from free love to safe sex is part of our experience.[18]

Katie Roiphe feels that there is a danger that 'bad sex' will be labelled 'rape'. She is uneasy about statements by Catherine MacKinnon. Professor of Law at Michigan University, who has said: 'I call it rape whenever a woman has sex and she feels violated.'[19] In other words, if a woman and a man have sex and the woman feels negative about the experience afterwards, can she now tell everyone she has been 'date raped'?

Men are confused and uncertain
Shere Hite, in *The Hite Report on the Family*, published in

1994, also describes a crisis in male identity. Writing in the *Guardian*, she says: 'There is a giant identity crisis in the western male soul, of which the recent widespread "return to traditionalism" is only a symptom'; however, she does not believe it can be solved by 'appealing to family values', which she sees as where 'the female is kept subservient and the male emotionally impoverished'. Hite says: 'A new kind of male heroism is required, a reinvention of the male psyche, a fresh identity for contemporary culture to reflect. I can't wait to see what it will be.'[20] In other words, the pendulum is definitely swinging towards traditional values, but Hite hopes that the end result will be something completely new.

Some would say that the 'new man'[21] has already arrived – willing to spend as much time as women on household chores, washing-up and laundry, changing nappies and cooking – yet still able to change a spark plug, clear a drain, put up a book shelf and carry heavy loads. Others would say that such men are still rare. In the meantime, confusion over roles continues, some of it because the abuse of sexual power means that various aspects of male identity have become suspect in the eyes of some people.

A consent form as well as a condom

It has been suggested that to avoid future trouble in a new relationship, a man should ask at each stage for consent to continue. After a 1992 New Jersey Supreme Court hearing on a teenager charged with rape of a girl he asked out, the deputy Public Defender of the case, Suan Herman, said: 'You not only have to bring a condom on a date, you have to bring a consent form as well.'[22]

Here we have the makings of a radical new culture, influenced by the extremes of feminism. It is a culture where a man goes slowly, respects the personal space of a woman before starting to make love, and is slightly uncertain and vulnerable when he begins to touch a woman he likes; where a man continues to feel under considerable tension throughout sex in a non-stable relationship. Sounds familiar.

In fact, it sounds like a throwback to a generation or two before – or even further back in history. Katie Roiphe has dug out one guide for young ladies written in 1857, which describes sensible conduct when alone with young men. Ironically, a guide for students today written by radical feminists sounds not dissimilar.[23] It gives a caution regarding male advances, how to tell an amorous man politely to get lost, making sure you are not alone or somewhere where you can get help if you need to, keeping a modest distance, etc.

A new puritanism powered by feminism?

You might think these ideas were part of a new puritanism, but instead you find at its heart a new movement within feminism. A further extension of this new thinking has been over the issue of sexual harassment. This also centres on the abuse of sexual power and the fear of acting insensitively. It is yet another factor profoundly affecting relationships between men and women. If a man compliments a woman on her new hairstyle, is that sexual harassment? What about a wolf whistle? A hand on a shoulder? A saucy joke? A rude calendar? Catherine MacKinnon was responsible for making some forms of sexual harassment legally actionable in the United States.[24]

The case of Judge Clarence Thomas from Oklahoma, accused of sexual harassment by Anita Hill, dominated the US press throughout 1991 and 1992. Then came accusations by 24 women against Oregon's Republican Senator Bob Packwood;[25] the sexual abuse of a large group of women by men of the US Navy at the infamous

Tailhook convention; and more recently, in 1994, the accusations against President Clinton by Paula Jones that he sexually harassed her at Little Rock in 1991.[26] Never before has sexual harassment been so publicly debated in the United States.[27]

Then there was the British case of Alison Halford, fighting sexual discrimination in the police force.[28] Not only did she finally win a settlement, but her action also prompted an independent enquiry that found nine out of ten female police officers had experienced sexual harassment at work.[29]

A recent UK survey on sexual harassment discovered that many men are now much more sensitive to the issue than women: men and women were asked to register approval or disapproval to six male behaviours ranging from calling someone 'love' or 'darling' to 'repeated sexual advances'. In all six categories, men were more disapproving than women. For example, 27 per cent of men thought pin-up posters of nude women on the walls were a form of sexual harassment, compared to only 16 per cent of women.[30] The Los Angeles Fire Department recently made headlines after banning staff from reading *Playboy*, *Penthouse* and similar magazines as a violation of women's rights.[31]

Sexual harassment and date rape have made people supersensitive to sexual power abuse, with a knock-on effect when it comes to sex itself, an effect that is adding to the forces directing sexual behaviour for a new generation. However, there is another dimension to sexual freedom that is also being challenged by feminism: the freedom to produce, buy and use erotic pornography.

Power feminism struggles with victim feminism

Over the last few years, two strands of feminism have

split over pornography. One part of the movement has always seen pornography as degrading, an insult to women who find themselves once more owned and controlled by a male-dominated world. Grave concerns have been expressed that the struggles by women against sexual violence and abuse are being undermined every day by an unrelenting diet of sexual images, encouraging men to abuse women, portraying women as creatures that exist only to satisfy their lust.

Catherine MacKinnon, like Andrea Dworkin, has attacked all forms of pornography. In her book *Only Words*, she says all pornography consists of acts of sexual discrimination or 'harm', in production, publication and use – even in private.[32]

However, other feminists would now say this argument is based on a 'victim' psychology: women are weak; women are abused; women are suffering every day; women need protecting from male pornography. The counter-argument of 'power feminism' goes something like this: women are the voting majority in many nations; women spend most of the household income and have purchasing power; women live longer, have a great capacity for sex and for multiple orgasms; women don't need protecting – so men had better watch out.

Power feminism prefers to turn the tables to redress the balance. It might find the idea of full-frontal men pin-up posters around the office rather amusing. Power feminism might prefer to organise an all-female party to go and watch a male stripper at a club, rather than ban all strip artists, photos and videos. This movement might want the freedom for women to call, if they wish, 'a handsome and well-developed escort providing fun times and massage',[33] or to join 1.6 million women across Europe attending 250,000 sex parties a year organised by Ann Summers Ltd, a thousand of which take place in Britain every week – women meeting in the sex shop equivalent of Tupperware parties in their own homes.[34]

Power feminism might be pleased to find that the drive for teenage sex may increasingly be coming from the girls rather than the boys. At one British school recently, an AIDS educator discovered that the boys in the class were acutely embarrassed at her suggestion that some girls might be putting pressure on them to have sex when sometimes they wanted to hold back.[35] They admitted it was true, even though it did not fit their own image. Before, a boy often tried to win a girl's favour and 'chased' her. Now, though, the girl may be chasing him.

In the balance of power between 'victim' and 'power' feminism, there is still a very strong anti-pornography movement within feminism that is increasingly vocal and confident. Added to this, the campaigns have been strengthened by a coalition of interest between different groups.

Victim feminism joins with right-wing anti-porn

Katie Roiphe sees Catherine MacKinnon's anti-porn campaign as 'the human bridge between the far right and the far left . . . the embodiment of an unholy alliance between the right wing and feminists'. In Britain, there have been private meetings between feminist and other anti-pornography campaigning groups, with both parties too embarrassed to disclose publicly that they are even talking.[36]

They combined efforts in a British campaign in 1990 to stop High Street stores from selling pornography. As a direct result, many retailers reduced their range of magazines: banning some, and restricting access to others or covering up the front pages.[37]

Labour front-bencher Clare Short campaigned against

'Page Three' of the *Sun* newspaper (semi-nude girls) in a way that received support from some colleagues in the Conservative Party, and derision from other colleagues who wanted to prop up the tabloid Tory press. In 1986, Clare Short introduced the first stage of a Parliamentary Bill to outlaw topless newspaper pin-ups; and in 1994, after eight more years of campaigning, the *Sun*'s owner Rupert Murdoch said of Page Three: 'now it's getting a bit old-fashioned. One day it will come out.'[38]

Old-fashioned? Pornography is old-fashioned? This is no ordinary person's opinion, either. It is the internationally famous Australian media supremo Rupert Murdoch speaking, one of the world's most powerful figures in publishing and television. The campaigns are altering sexual fashion, winding back the clock regarding explicit sex. In the UK alone, Rupert Murdoch operates more channels than the whole BBC and Independent Television networks combined. This is someone with his finger constantly on the pulse of the ups and downs of popular culture. He is detecting a change, and the need to be ready to run with tomorrow's fashion. 'Page Three' will be out of it soon.

Clare Short was delighted: 'The tide of public opinion has switched,' she said, 'and it has been widely seen as grotty and demeaning.'[39]

Pornography advertises sex . . .

So, pornography is likely to be increasingly frowned upon in the new world of sexual relationships, but what is the evidence that pornography changes behaviour? Many would say it is degrading for women to be paid to expose their bodies for men to leer at or fantasise over, but does it really encourage rape or other sex abuse? Evidence suggests that it might – as does common sense. Dr Catherine Itzin, author of a new study on pornography, has said: 'While nobody in their right mind would claim that pornography is the sole cause of sexism and sexual violence, there is now enormous evidence that porn is linked to sexism and genital violence against women. If women are presented purely in terms of their genitals, how can they be seen as fully human and men's equals?'[40]

It is obvious to most people that pornography is likely to change behaviour, because we know advertising works. A friend of mine makes television commercials. He knows full well that a company will invest up to £1,000,000 to create the right 60 seconds of film. Every time the sequence is shown, they believe that hundreds – maybe thousands – of shoppers will go out and buy their product. Advertisers earn money by persuading companies that they can control the behaviour of millions. They can prove it with marketing surveys: the campaign starts in the north, and within a week, all outlets are reporting rising sales. The campaign moves south – sales increase 20 per cent there during the campaign, and so on. Any successful advertising agency can give you numerous examples of such stories.

The evidence from advertising is so striking that the burden of proof should fall on the pornography industry itself to convince us it has no effect. If a repeated 30-second advert can alter the behaviour of millions, then what does a three-hour film do? What is the effect of a hundred such films in as many days? Many film makers have been concerned that home video allows the same five-minute sequences in a three-hour film to be watched a hundred times over. Thus the effect of just one scene in a whole film can be amplified beyond all recognition. Many of these films promote a fantasy of women desperate to have sex with men, of group sex, and sex involving violence.

Adults may be relatively resistant to the power of such repeated images, but what about teenagers or young children, who may watch whatever brothers, sisters or parents bring home? Research has discovered that pornography can alter the mind. Sex porn is designed to arouse, to excite men. Arousal prepares the body for sex, and therefore porn by definition is likely to make men want to have sex soon after exposure to it. Arousal also decreases inhibitions, altering perceptions, and awakening powerful latent feelings in both men and women.

Non-violent pornography can make men aggressive or euphoric, or both. In 1993, Prerost at Western Illinois University studied 90 men after exposure to sexual music videos, rock videos and a travel documentary, and found elation and aggression scores increased after erotic sequences – especially in those feeling guilty.[41] That was the effect after one laboratory session, but what about after someone watches ten or twelve hours non-stop of this material at home? What happens to the mind, imagination and emotions then? What if the person already has very unhealthy thoughts about violent or degrading sex?

Zillman found male students were more likely to be callous towards women and to trivialise rape. Weaver found women more likely to be perceived as sex objects and men to recommend lighter sentences for rape.

The Meese Commission Report claimed exposure to pornography could lead to sex crimes. In 1993, Nutter and Kearns interviewed sex offenders and compared them to non-offenders. They found sex offenders began masturbating at a younger age, and that sexually explicit materials were used by them in their first masturbatory experience by one in three, compared to only one in seven of the others.[42] However, they found no difference in adult use of pornography between offenders and others.

Pornography, the theory? Rape, the practice?
In 1991, Kutchinsky in Denmark set out to test Morgan's

statement of 1980 that 'pornography is the theory, rape is the practice'. The original US Commission on Obscenity and Pornography in 1970 found no link, but what about more recent evidence? Kutchinsky discovered that a number of different studies clearly showed that some men became aggressive following exposure to sex scenes containing violence, but found no difference in sexual arousal in rapists, non-sexual criminals or non-criminal males after watching sex scenes,[43] although this study's conclusions have been heavily criticised by others.

However, he then reviewed rape and reported rape figures in America, Denmark, Sweden and West Germany from 1964 to 1984, during a time when availability of pornography changed 'from extreme scarcity to relative abundance'. He found that rape figures increased rapidly in each country. He then compared this rise to the rise in other violent crime, and found they were of the same order, leading him to conclude that it was hard to blame pornography on that evidence alone.[44]

Another large study was to provide new disturbing evidence of a link. In 1990, Baron and Straus found huge differences in rape figures across 50 US states between 1980 and 1982. What differences in areas could be responsible? Were they related to crime rate differences, sexual inequality in different states, differences in consumption of pornography, or differences in attitudes towards violence? Results suggested possible links with all four, but local use of pornography was implicated as an important contributor to risk of rape in any area.[45] This was measured by the volume of sales in proportion to the population.

While scientific evidence of a proven link between crime and pornography will never be 100 per cent conclusive, the anecdotes continue. In some cases, these are of a link between erotic pornography and sex crimes; in others, a possible link is suggested between violent pornography and violent crime – or a mixture of the two. Either way, the evidence seems to be growing that what people watch can affect their behaviour. For example, in March 1994, four Welsh youths were convicted of kicking a father to death after he told them to stop vandalising a traffic bollard. His injuries were so severe that doctors thought he had been hit by a car. After the attack, one youth told a friend: 'When you have a fight, you don't stop stamping until they are dead.' When he was told the man *was* dead, the youth replied: 'I hope so.' Two of the accused sprayed their names in aerosol paint at the scene, and one of the gang yelled moments after the attack: 'I've got the juice.'[46] Police believe the youths were influenced by a cult video about gang warfare in the United States, which they had watched immediately before the murder. The film was called *Juice*. What they yelled seemed to come straight from the film, or was it just a coincidence?

In the same month, another thirteen-year-old boy was in court after attacking a six-year-old girl, leading her into a field and sexually abusing her. The boy admitted it all, and said he intended to have sex with her. His defence barrister said that the boy felt he was abnormal not to have a girlfriend, and had an 'unhealthy' interest in pornographic magazines or computer discs brought into school by other boys.

Some computer porn is 'official', marketed on CD laser discs called CD-Roms, such as the Interactive Lover's Guide, with moving images so explicit that they would be illegal on video. Computer porn can also be carried on ordinary magnetic disks, made and distributed through underground networks, or Internet.[47] The accused boy thought it was normal to have sex with girls his age and younger, and pornographic material was said to have 'pushed him over the edge'.[48] It was pointed out that computer images are extremely difficult to regulate.[49]

Child psychologists vote against pornography

So, then, there is some research to support a link between pornography and undesirable sexual behaviour, much anecdotal evidence, and indirect evidence from advertising and marketing – enough to make 26 leading child psychologists change their minds in April 1994, after arguing for years that no link existed;[50] enough to send the British government into a massive about-turn a week later, agreeing to stronger regulation for 'video nasties',[51] with labels showing age for viewing, and degree of violence, language, sex/nudity, as well as theme.[52]

Tough fines were introduced for renting videos to under-age children,[53] and members of all political parties had been campaigning for this for some time.[54] Others said controls were useless because they were easily evaded, and anyway they would 'censor film art and ban certain classic films'.[55] In another sign of change, Mary Whitehouse, long-time campaigner against media sex and violence, was recently introduced on BBC Radio 1 music station as 'the lady who everyone hated in the 70s and 80s and got up everyone's nose, and now many people are saying was right all along'.[56]

Regulations on films in the United Kingdom are already some of the strictest in Europe. In Spain and Portugal, any censorship is illegal. Films are classified, but not cut – and cannot be banned. In Greece there are no classifications; in Sweden, the top classification age is 15; in Holland and Denmark, it is 16, and Germany and France are far more relaxed than the British.[57]

The new controls in Britain were further evidence of a change in thinking about sexual power abuse and pressure, a new age beginning to dawn, a nation waking from slumber to reject a slide to current European values on sex in the media, and to say 'enough is enough'.

Teachers warn parents over child exposure

Despite the conservative views of many parents, some almost seem to encourage their children to watch adult films and programmes by allowing television-viewing in bedrooms at night, or by leaving adult videos lying around.[58] When teachers mention to parents that their children as young as age eight are watching adult material, some shrug it off. One primary teacher said: 'I've heard children under seven say they watch these films with their uncles and cousins who are aged 18 to 25.'[59]

Sex films and ones containing extreme violence are having an increasingly obvious effect on children's minds. Teachers say adult films are destroying innocence and giving children nightmares, with sexual confusion, listlessness and hyperactivity. Others report young pupils simulating sex in the playground. When asked what her favourite film was from the Christmas vacation, one eight-year-old said it was *Silence of the Lambs* – an extremely violent and disturbing adult film.[60]

There is another side to the debate. For example, in 1994 the Policy Studies Institute was asked by the British Board of Film Classification to compare television viewing habits of persistent young offenders with non-offenders. They found very little difference.[61] However, the two groups were not strictly comparable, and the study excluded videos. Many young offenders were found to have lives 'that were full of change, chaos and deprivation, in which the media were of less significance than was the case for non-offending peers'.

Despite this, James Ferman, Director of the British Board of Film Classification, said that the rising tide of violent images available to children frightened him.

Britain was becoming a 'media saturated nation', in which it was impossible to protect vulnerable and impressionable children from the violence and pornography surrounding them. 'With video, cable and satellite, the cinema has moved to the sitting room, and it is impossible to monitor the viewing of a young person.' Ferman pointed to a recent report where young children had ransacked a neighbour's house after watching similar behaviour on video:[62] 'This demonstrates how vulnerable people are. It is astonishing to me that people are surprised. Children will imitate anything they see . . . I am frightened for the future. In my job I am walking a tightrope, trying to please people who want freedom of expression and people who want stricter controls.'[63]

In Britain, it has meant rows between different censors over such things as degree of exposure of genitalia allowed.[64] As soon as the government crack-down on videos was announced, James Ferman commented: 'from now on we are going to have to cut more and classify higher'.[65] However, all classification systems collapse under the barrage of satellite transmissions that are censor free. Any child with satellite television at home is increasingly likely to have access to a wide range of foreign channels, more so perhaps with cable. Many of these are from other European countries, with more relaxed rules on how much can be shown in sex scenes. The old distinction over transmission times between child and adult viewing also breaks down in any home where a child can programme the clock on a video.

Child pornography is a growth industry

If there have been concerns about adult pornography that are adding pressure for change, there is almost universal unease about the growth of children taking part in pornography, the growth of paedophilia, and sex rings as a further expression of sexual freedom.[66] Subtle traces of paedophilia are drifting into the edge of respectability. For example, sexually exciting images of adults dressed as school children became a fashion craze in the mid-1990s in some countries, causing controversy in the fashion world. The *Independent* reported: 'Grown women everywhere are wearing children's cutie-pie clothes that look as though they shrank in the wash.'[67]

However, the real worry is sexual exploitation of children filmed in various states of undress in positions designed to be sexually exciting to paedophiles. In the United States, the 1984 Child Protection Act gave new federal powers to prosecute people involved in distribution, receipt and possession of child pornography. Previously, the laws were the same as for adult pornography.[68] This new Act greatly reduced the availability, according to Len Munsil, executive director of the National Family Legal Foundation, driving sales underground. The big question, though, is one of definition: is nudity necessary for conviction?

In the UK, the 1978 Protection of Children Act, amended by the Criminal Justice Act of 1988, made possession of child pornography materials an offence, as well as distribution of it.

In the historic Knox case in 1991, it was said that all material was illegal if it involved sexual exploitation of children. However, this was contested by the Clinton administration, paving the way for partially clothed images of children to be sold again with legal backing.[69]

It is ironic that with more open displays of affection between adults, and a relaxed sexual code, fears of child sex abuse have begun to inhibit parents from touching or hugging their children or allowing young children to see them naked. Sexual freedom has therefore backfired to produce inhibition, prudery and neuroticism.

Can I hug my children?

Influential old Dr Spock was cautious about parental nudity in front of boys over the age of four in case it aroused feelings of anger, fear or guilt. 'As a general rule, keep reasonably covered and keep children out of the bathroom.' However, many households have had a far more relaxed attitude – at least, up until now.[70] Libby Purves wrote in The Times:

> Fewer fathers now dare pick up their daughter's small friends or help them in the swimming pool. Fathers and uncles stifle their instinct to wrestle and cuddle. The children half-choke in the dense smoke too: after a newspaper report of child molestation, one innocent young father distressed his four year old and his wife – who told me the story – by refusing to stay in bed for the regular morning cuddle. He would leap out of bed and dress, as ashamed as a modern Adam . . . Men teachers are warned by their Unions not to comfort a distressed child physically or talk to one in a room alone . . . Those with no fathers at home may never learn that a grown man can be tender, and lend the strength of his arm to their weakness. Their daily mentors have been made too afraid that a hug or a steadying hand might be 'inappropriate'.[71]

The result is 'touch-starved' children: children not only experiencing loss of parental attention following separation or divorce, but also loss of open affection. This can only make more acute the great search for love we saw earlier, and the pressures to find a substitute for family affection in sex.[72] It is a strange irony that we live in an age that forbids or discourages parental affection, while our culture encourages 16-year-olds to have sex with one another. Surely something has gone seriously wrong?

A new awareness of sexual power and how it can be abused has stuck a further spear in the sexual revolution. The sexual revolution has failed to deliver equality in sexual relationships. Instead, we see soaring figures for rape and other sex crimes, which makes many wonder if all the revolution did was remove a helpful restraint on sexual power, encouraging violence and abuse.

However, there is another huge area that is shaping a new sexual age: the pressure to perform – a pressure that is also now backfiring.

The pressure to perform

The pressure to perform sexually is enormous and destructive, but what do people mean by performance anyway? For some, it means having adequate sexual equipment to start with.

A group of teenagers were separated into their respective sexes and asked various questions. The boys were asked what they thought girls were looking for in someone they fancied, while next door the girls were asked the same question. The two groups were then gathered back into a larger group for feedback. The boys were in for a shock. Their main idea was that girls were interested in performance – the size of their erections, strength, physical prowess. Yet the girls said they were looking for friendship, someone who would treat them with respect, listen to them, and be fun to be with. To them, equipment size scored almost nothing – good looks certainly, but that's a different thing.

The opinion of the girls is identical to their parents. A 1993 Gallup Poll conducted by the *Daily Telegraph* of 1,014 women aged between 18 and 60 found that what women wanted most at home was an equal relationship with a loyal, reliable husband, closely followed by a desire for understanding, someone who would share their concerns.

When they were asked what they would first look for in a male partner, 35 per cent said sense of humour, 23 per cent loyalty, 10 per cent affection, 7 per cent ability to discuss emotions, 7 per cent good looks, 2 per cent charm, and a mere 1 per cent for a good lover.[73] Once married, only 28 per cent said sex was 'very important', a further 57 per cent said 'quite important'. And as we have seen earlier, two-thirds said they would not forgive a single act of infidelity.[74]

Teenage insecurity about appearance and performance

Many teenage girls are insecure regarding their own appearance – seen at its extreme in anorexia nervosa, where a girl slowly exterminates her sexuality as she starves herself – sometimes to the point of death. As body weight falls, the process that triggers puberty is reversed, hormone levels fall to those in a child, ovulation stops, breasts shrink, body fat disappears, and menstruation becomes a distant memory.

Yet physique is different from performance. Apart from body building for men, or diets, workouts and cosmetics for girls, there is less you can do about physique than performance. Yet performance can be learned, so we are told. Every woman is entitled to a multiple orgasm. Every man should be able to get an erection whenever he wants, wherever he wants, and for as long as he needs. Every woman can satisfy her man, and every man can satisfy his woman.

But the stakes are growing, and so are the pressures.

'Can't get no satisfaction'

What exactly is satisfaction and how do you measure it? Satisfaction is a comparative thing. The curse of comparison is that however rich or poor we are, whether we live in an African village or Manhattan, in a London squat or in Belgravia, we can always compare ourselves with those who have more. The curse of comparison catapults us into consumer madness, forever leapfrogging over our neighbours because in the pecking order of our own minds we should be further on than them. The result is guaranteed dissatisfaction, guaranteed hunger for more, and guaranteed frustration. If this is true generally in a consumerist world, then it is just as true of sex. In fact, you could say that the entire drive for the sexual revolution has been powered by a dangled carrot of 'more in store'.

But there is a very big difference. When it comes to wealth, technology can provide more and more goods to satisfy our demand. When it comes to sex, though, things are different There are only a finite number of ways of having sex. We have all been treated to graphic descriptions of 101 better positions to try next time, but all the sex books in the world are likely to leave the person either bored or dissatisfied. Bored that they have seen it all, felt it all, done it all, yet are still left wondering whether the mega-effort was worth it.

When you've tried everything, what then? The bored are told to do better, and then they will come alive in a new way. The dissatisfied are told they or their partners are failures in need of more lessons.

A mind-set is being created that by definition cannot fully be satisfied. That is why the sex guides and agony columns sell and sell – and also, because they entertain and amuse. But will sex sell for ever?

Madonna is in recession

Madonna, with her raunchy images of sex, has been a music industry icon of the late 1980s and early 1990s, ever since she began exposing her belly-button. Yet Madonna is now in recession, as more and more people realise that sexual freedom can be boring and bland. Her album *Erotica* tumbled quickly in the charts, and two singles from *Erotica*, 'Rain' and 'Bad Girl', peaked at only no. 30 and no. 36 respectively. Her next film is *Snake Eyes*, which is yet more sex after *In Bed with Madonna* – but will the old formula work?[75] Will images of lesbianism work any better?

In February 1994, the *Los Angeles Times* surveyed leading US record company executives to find out what artists or groups they would most like to sign if they could. Madonna was rated just thirteenth, after Whitney Houston (sixth) and Janet Jackson (twelfth). One said: 'She's probably the marketing genius of all time, but I think she out-geniused herself with the book [*Sex*], the movie [*Body of Evidence*] and the album [*Erotica*]. There's really a backlash. I feel sorry for her.'[76] The general view is that Madonna is over-exposed. As her popular appeal declines, she is being discovered by academia – perhaps the surest sign that she is passé. Sex may not guarantee twenty-first century sales.

If the agony columns are anything to go by, 40 years of so-called liberation have left millions feeling as frustrated, confused and curious as ever. There is no evidence that the sexual revolution has made us happier or more contented. Indeed, you could even argue the opposite. Dr Peter Dally, consultant psychiatrist at Westminster Hospital in London, wrote in 1990:

> Surely, then, with such apparent social tolerance, with men and women sexually liberated and comparatively free to do as they choose, there should be a much wider sense of contentment and well-being. Yet the discontent and the mental and physical disorders that arise from unsatisfactory sex lives do not seem to lessen. On the contrary, from the point of view of a doctor, they seem to be on the increase. For although the extreme prudery

and sexual repression associated with the Victorian era have largely vanished, the essential problems inherent in any sexual relationship are no different.[77]

In 1971, the Samaritans in the United Kingdom had only 89,000 calls from depressed and suicidal people. Twenty years on in the sexual revolution, the numbers had soared to 470,000.[78]

Sex magazines turn to younger girls

While adults may eventually reach saturation point, there will always be a new generation reaching puberty for whom sex is a great discovery. Many sex magazines are now targeting this market.

Recently I took part in a one- and a-half-hour radio debate on magazines for teenage girls. The other guest was the editor of one magazine and agony aunt of another. The big question was this: were her magazines just 'going with the flow' or were they corrupting propaganda, promoting under-age sex to the young?

The editor claimed that the magazines were aimed mainly at older teenagers, but I knew otherwise. Just an hour before I had jumped out of a cab on the way to the studio and run into a corner shop that sold a large range of them. I asked the sales assistant for a copy of whatever 11–15-year-olds were buying, and came away with around ten different magazines. It's obvious that no self-respecting 17-year-old girl is going to be seen dead walking out of a shop with a magazine called *Just Seventeen* – the name itself is a nonsense.

On the programme, 12- and 13-year-old girls and boys phoned in to give their own views, the majority of which were overwhelmingly negative. One girl said she thought it was stupid to put out sex, sex, and more sex, when teenage pregnancies and sexual diseases were so rampant.

The editor replied that sex sells, and magazines are 'only reflecting where young people are at'.

I read out a few of the headlines from these teenage magazines:

'Women only love me for my willy – one man's BIG problem' – front page.[79]

'I charge £10,000 for sex – confessions of a gigolo' – also front page.[80]

'Well-groomed and well-horny.'[81]

'Battle of the strippers – an evening of body oil and G-strings.'[82]

'Sexy standups – and we're gagging for more – six comedians sound off on life, love and laughing women into bed.'[83]

'Real life photo story – he wanted to go all the way.'[84]

'His hand was up my blouse when my mum walked in.'[85]

'They called me out of class to tell me my baby was dying – a 14-year-old mum's heartbreaking story.'[86]

'Hot lovers!'[87]

'Photo story – he only wanted a one night stand.'[88]

'If I want sex, I go out and get it – why three girls have one night stands – the feeling, the fascination, the freedom!'[89]

Nine-year-olds read this stuff

We have already seen how grossly misleading all this is in the light of large-scale surveys showing how unexpectedly little sexual activity is going on among teenagers.[90] The fuss is because these magazines seem intent on propelling teenagers into premature sex.

The day after the programme, our 11-year-old son John went into my office at the top of our house, and saw my case bulging open with loads of these magazines. His eyes popped out of his head. 'Dad,' he yelled, 'what's all this stuff in your case?' Caroline, our nine-year-old, rushed upstairs to inspect it, and then said dismissively, 'Oh, *that* stuff – my friends all read those things in the playground.'

One magazine aimed at the 13–16-year-old market had a big three-page feature with photographs: 'My sister and I got pregnant by the same boy – when 15-year-old Kerry . . . found out her little sister (13) was pregnant, she couldn't believe her ears . . .'[91] There was just *one* sentence of comment at the end: 'Kerry and Andrea are very lucky to have the support of their mum, but having a baby at a young age isn't easy. For confidential advice . . . contact address . . .'

For any rebellious teenager, this was a powerful, positive image of a girl, an anti-hero, a national celebrity, lots of attention – all the authorities up in arms, yet showering attention on her for the sake of the baby.

Pregnant pupils are no role models

Attempts have been made in the classroom to use 15-year-olds with babies as part of sex education, in order to warn teenagers of the risks. However, I am concerned that they may be seen as having special status, attractive as role models.[92]

Magazines aimed at teenagers do have a key role in education, particularly for girls (who are more likely to read them), but there is no need to pack so much explicit erotic material into them. Child psychotherapist Jeanine said: 'The internal pressures on young people because of these magazines are huge. When there is an emotional gap and they feel unloved, there is added pressure for early sexual experience.'

As we have seen, the search for love can be directly

related to teenage sex and pregnancy.[93] Dr Peter Dally has said:

> Children may feel deprived of love and become unsure of themselves, so their emotional development suffers . . . The child, and later adult, feels empty and is forever seeking love, for reassurance that he or she is indeed good and lovable. Such a neurotic need can rarely be satisfied, and it must be contrasted with real, adult love, in which another person is loved for his or her own sake, not just for the emotional response. A young woman had a reputation for being a nymphomaniac . . . Sex for her was an endless search to prove she was lovable and wanted by others.[94]

This particular woman eventually committed suicide.

It is no good just giving information on contraception if a teenage girl finds the idea of being pregnant attractive. Some community workers I know tried to support a troubled teenager who left home. After a few weeks in a homeless hostel, she announced with pride that she was pregnant. In her eyes, perhaps, she now had identity and importance: she would have someone to love, a family of her own.

One 16-year-old was interviewed recently, and said she 'just wanted a baby' and had planned it, although she was not really sure why.[95] As a commentator put it: 'This may be the really thorny problem for the government: not whether girls should be given sex education or not, but trying to persuade them there might be something more worthwhile to do with their lives.'[96]

On BBC *Panorama* in 1993, one 15-year-old girl created a storm of controversy by saying she had got pregnant to get away from school, and then again to get a council home.[97] Such things may be rare, but they are very disturbing.

Others are ignorant about sex

It is also true that many teenagers are ignorant. Doreen Massey, the Director of the Family Planning Association, described recently how some youngsters still believe 'you can't get pregnant the first time', or, 'it's OK if you do it standing up, or after a period'.[98] The agony Aunt Claire Rayner said recently: 'I am still getting too many letters from girls who say they became pregnant as though it was something that just happened.'[99] With more than 70,000 teenagers pregnant each year, every large secondary school in the country can expect classroom pregnancies and babies almost every year.

Pressures are so great to find a solution that British health ministers have been considering a morning-after pill to go on sale to teenagers in pharmacies.[100] It has fewer side effects and a lower risk to health than a conventional abortion, and works by preventing implantation.

The government is taking the issue of teenage pregnancy increasingly seriously. It aims to halve the number of conceptions in under-16-year-olds from the one in a hundred in 1989 to one in two hundred by the year 2000,[101] and the rates are already starting to fall. It believes that parents have a vital role – and so do their children. Most 13–14-year-olds in one survey of 29,000 teenagers in Britain said they would prefer sex education from their parents, but find it hard to talk to them.[102]

I am not arguing for short-changing young people on formal sex education, although the role of parents is vital. As we have seen, I was responsible for starting an agency that is currently providing more resources for British schools on sex/HIV education than the whole of the government programme. The answer, as we have seen, is to provide clear, factual sex education in the context of relationships, commitment, family values and helping young people feel able to make choices about their own lives by resisting peer pressure, and feeling secure about themselves.

So, then, we have seen that the sexual revolution is in big trouble. While sex can provide pleasure so intense it can be addictive, frustration and dissatisfaction are also very common, and so is the continued search for a romantic ideal of a long-term relationship. We have seen that the 1960s generation have grown up to want something different for their teenage children, and that their children are being surprisingly conservative and sexually inactive.

We have seen how sexual freedom has often led to power being abused, with growing concern about rape and other forms of sexual tyranny; how *his* freedom can be *her* loss of freedom, one person's freedom to express sexual desire can be another's nightmare, how young people often feel under great pressure to be sexually active, to be accepted in their own eyes as normal; and how teenage pregnancy is a big issue, and how many are using sex as a substitute for love.

But the revolution in sexual relationships is in a far greater crisis than this for many other reasons, the most obvious being that sexual chaos can make you very ill or even kill you.

4

SEX AND SICKNESS

When people today think of sexual disease, they tend to think of AIDS,[1] but there is nothing new about being ill as a result of sex. Syphilis caused death, disfigurement, chronic illness, diseased babies and other problems right from the start of the first epidemic in Europe in 1494, which later caused such havoc that the French army was disbanded. Some would even trace sexual illnesses from biblical times.

It was only in 1658 that the terrible plague was correctly linked to sex. It remained a serious threat to public health, and a major cause of death until the discovery of penicillin by Sir Alexander Fleming in 1929 and its first effective use in fighting infection in 1941.[2]

During the Second World War, there was a poster of Hitler and Mussolini arm in arm with a prostitute, with the caption: 'VD, worst of the three'. At the beginning of the war, syphilis treatments were still relatively ineffective.

Yet despite the miracle of penicillin-based drugs, and despite the fact that, unlike multiple-resistant gonorrhoea, syphilis remains very sensitive to penicillin, we have today the largest syphilis epidemic this world has ever seen.

Sexual diseases out of control

The sheer scale of sexually transmitted diseases (STDs) world-wide is hard to comprehend: trichomoniasis, syphilis, chancroid, chlamydia, herpes, genital warts, and a host of other illnesses are modern-day plagues in every single nation of the world. According to the World Health Organisation, there are at least 250 million new cases of STDs every year throughout the world.[3] This is made up of 120 million with trichomoniasis, 50 million with genital chlamydia, 30 million with genital papillomavirus (implicated in cervical cancer), 25 million with gonorrhoea, 20 million with genital herpes, 3.5 million with syphilis, 2 million with chancroid, and more than 2 million new cases of HIV[4] annually. These numbers are so large that they can seem meaningless.

In Britain, 580,000 are treated with a new STD every year – an increase of 21 per cent on the 1981 figure.[5] Some of these are the same people returning more than once with new infections. STDs increased each year by 35 per cent from 1981 to 1986, then fell a little during the first AIDS awareness campaigns, although rising again in 1989 and 1990. By 1990, there was one visit to a sex disease clinic for every 50 adults; some were repeat visits.

The pattern of sexual diseases changed dramatically between 1981 and 1990.[6] Genital warts rose 190 per cent in women, and 120 per cent in men. Genital herpes rose 110 per cent in women, 90 per cent in men, while syphilis and gonorrhoea declined by 65 per cent and 86 per cent respectively, rising again more recently. Warts and herpes are caused by viruses for which there is no cure, and high-risk behaviour is once again increasing in some groups (particularly among younger gay men). However, as we have seen, it is still true that among teenage heterosexuals there is less sexual activity occurring than some media reporting has indicated.

Rest of Europe and the United States hard hit

In Europe, STDs are now second only to chest and throat infections as a cause of illness due to infection.[7] Much of this increase in sickness is due to the longer-term effects of sexual diseases in women – for example, chronic pelvic inflammatory disease (PID), or is due to growing numbers of infected foetuses and newborn babies.[8]

In the United States, there are 12 million new cases of STDs annually, two-thirds in under-25-year-olds, and a quarter in teenagers. Gonorrhoea and syphilis are common in 14–16-year-olds in New York detention centres.[9] Over 30 million may be infected with genital herpes, for which there is no cure, while one in five adults may be infected at any time with at least one STD.[10] Many other nations have similar or higher rates.

Sex is an ideal way for germs to travel. The biggest problem for microbes and viruses is survival during transfer and transport. However, the sexual act is a most intimate fusion of two human bodies, bringing warm, thick secretions together, mixing them, rubbing them deeply into layers of the thinnest, most fragile areas of the body. During sex, the virus or microbe is gently cared for at all times in one body fluid before mixing with another, hence it is the ideal way for germs to travel. The virus is never exposed to the rigours of the outside world; it is kept at an ideal constant temperature, and has constant access either to cells for which it is designed, or nutrients in which to grow. There is one other factor too: most people have sex with each other many times over, and therefore spread becomes almost guaranteed with time.

The many different diseases

Most people who attend STD clinics in countries like the United Kingdom have inflammation of the urinary tract, for which no cure can be found: so-called non-specific urethritis (NSU).[11] Many cases turn out to be caused by chlamydia trachomatis or trichomonas vaginalis.[12] Chlamydia can cause infertility in women and prostatitis in men. Not all cases of NSU are sexually transmitted, though.

There are a great number of different organisms that spread through sex. Here is a partial list; it varies from country to country.

Gonorrhoea

Gonorrhoea is an ancient disease, and the first cases of gonorrhoea may have been described in the Old Testament.[13] The first sign is usually pain or burning on passing water, although there may be no symptoms at all, particularly in women. Pus appears after five days or more, followed by healing and scarring, with narrowing of the urethra through which the urine passes.

Gonorrhoea can infect the Bartholin's glands in women, causing a big painful abscess at the entrance to the vagina, and can infect the cervix, resulting in a discharge. It can spread up through the uterus to the fallopian tubes, causing acute, intensely painful infection with a fever. From there, the organisms can enter the internal body cavity (peritoneum), causing pus to collect around the ovaries and fallopian tubes (pelvic inflammatory disease). This can take months to settle down completely, leaving scarring and infertility.[14]

In men, gonorrhoea can cause infection of the prostate and other glands, and in both sexes the throat and rectum can also become inflamed. Gonorrhoea can cause arthritis and septicaemia when the bacteria enter the bloodstream, making the person very ill with fever, pain in the joints, skin rashes and inflammation of the eyes.

In 95 per cent of cases, early infection is cured by a single injection of penicillin. However, in the mid-1970s, reports began to appear of resistant strains. So far, no strain has yet emerged that is resistant to all commonly used antibiotics.[15]

Granuloma inguinale

Granuloma inguinale causes swelling of the genitalia and a narrowing of the urethra, the channel that urine travels through. It starts as a small raised bump, with pain, burning, itching and discharge from the affected area. The infection can spread to affect internal organs, especially in women. It can also spread with large advancing ulcers down the thighs, or up on to the abdominal wall. Other infections often follow, producing a large, foul-smelling ulcer that is very difficult to treat.

The disease is found in black-skinned people in the tropics, West Africa, northern Australia, China and the southern part of the United States. It also occurs in India, Indonesia, the Pacific Islands, South America and the Caribbean. It is treated with antibiotics and most cases can be cured. In resistant cases, a massive extension of the ulcers occurs, with bleeding, wasting and eventual death.[16]

Thrush

Many infections can cause irritation of the vagina or surrounding skin in a woman, or the surface of the penis in a man. The surface becomes red and inflamed, and in a woman there can be a thick discharge. It is commonly caused by a yeast called candida, with symptoms known as thrush. It is spread sexually between partners, but thrush can erupt spontaneously without sexual activity. The candida yeast lives on all of our bodies anyway, and thrush is easily treated.

Chancroid

Chancroid is the commonest STD in some parts of the world, although rare in temperate countries. It is characterised by painful, soft ulcers on the genitalia; these break down, creating open sores that discharge, forming larger, ragged craters. Other lesions then develop; these bleed easily.

The lymph nodes in the groin become enlarged and painful, and then finally break open as an abscess discharging pus. The person can have chills, a fever and feel very ill. Healing does take place, but only after a lot of scarring – which can be very disfiguring to the genitalia. There are many different antibiotic treatments. If one fails, another is very likely to work.[17]

Genital herpes

Herpetic ulceration is caused by herpes virus type II. There is an incubation period of four or five days, after which the skin becomes itchy and sore. A few hours later it becomes red, and small pale blisters begin to appear. These then burst, and can form large painful ulcers covered with crusts. During the first attack, which is usually more severe, the lymph nodes in the groin also swell and are tender, and there may be headache and fever. The blisters are highly infectious until healed, which may take two weeks. Further attacks are likely, although they tend to be less acute. The virus hides in nerves, and can be reactivated by sexual intercourse, menstruation, stress, tiredness or other illnesses.

If a woman is acutely infected during pregnancy, there is an increased risk of miscarriage or congenital abnormalities, or infection of the baby during birth. There may also be an increased risk of cervical cancer from the virus. The anti-viral drug acyclovir can shorten the length of an attack and moderate the intensity, but there is no cure. The attack subsides in time, when the virus returns to hide in the nerves once more.

Genital warts and other viruses

Genital warts are caused by human papilloma virus. These highly infectious lumps often have a 'cauliflower' appearance, and may require many visits to a clinic to try and get rid of them. This may involve putting substances on the skin to 'burn' them away, such as podophyllum resin, or cryosurgery (freezing the skin). The virus is thought to cause cancer of the cervix, vulva, penis and anus in a minority of those infected. The warts spread sexually between partners, with an average incubation period of eight weeks.[18]

Human T-cell lymphotrophic virus can also be sexually transmitted, causing leukaemia, lymphoma, or tropical spastic paraparesis.

Molluscum contagiosum virus causes raised bumps on the skin of the genitalia, filled with a cheesy material.

Pelvic inflammatory disease (PID) and others

Pelvic inflammatory disease is very common, and accounts for up to 20 per cent of all gynaecological consultations.[19] The damage from internal infection can produce a wide variety of chronic or acute symptoms, resulting in infertility among other things, and sometimes life-threatening pregnancies outside the womb. It can be caused by mycoplasma hominis, chlamydia and many other organisms.

Trichomonas vaginalis can cause vaginal inflammation, with profuse, thin, foamy, yellowish discharge, local burning and itching. The treatment is an antibiotic called metronidazole.

Reiter's disease or syndrome is caused by a variety of infections in the non-specific urethritis group. It consists of urethritis in men, or infection of the cervix in women, red inflamed eyes, pain in the joints (arthritis), skin rashes and inflammation of tendons. It can be severe enough to keep someone in hospital, and in so much pain that movement is difficult. Treatment is with antibiotics and rest.

Crabs, lice and scabies

Some remarkable things can happen during sex. I remember as a medical student I was asked to see a man in a large casualty department who a nurse thought probably needed to see a psychiatrist. He told me he had a terrible problem: 'Millions of spiders are crawling up my legs.' He was deadly serious about it.

He invited me to inspect his thighs. He was quite right: hundreds of thousands of tiny biting insects were crawling all over his legs and his groin. Each one was the size of a pinhead. He had picked up pediculosis pubis, or pubic lice, from his previous partner. The treatment is a lotion of dicophane or malathion applied from the waist to the knees; this kills the insects. Just as pubic lice can be caught during sex, so can scabies, which is caused by tiny insects burrowing into the skin.

Syphilis

Syphilis is caused by treponema pallidum. It is known as the great mimic, because it can produce in advanced stages the signs of almost any illness you can think of: rashes, nerve damage, heart disease, disease of the blood vessels, brain damage, damage to the developing foetus, and infection of the newborn child. The first sign is a small painless red spot, which appears between one week and several months after infection.

The site eventually ulcerates, producing a painless crater that does not bleed. The lymph glands may also swell. The lesion is highly infectious, but heals over in a few weeks leaving a scar. The next 'secondary stage' can look like dermatitis, psoriasis, measles and scarlet fever, leprosy or flea bites. These things usually appear about two months after the original infection.

There can be a flu-like illness with tiredness and fever, aches and pains. Ulcers appear in the mouth, entrance to the vagina, and the tip of the penis. All signs then disappear, and that is the end of it in two out of three people. In the remainder, there may be a gap of as long as 20 years before further problems appear, with an attack on blood vessels, skin, bones, gut, nerves and brain, causing weakness, paralysis and eventual death if untreated. Penicillin is the treatment of choice.

Hepatitis B

In the 1970s, hepatitis B was thought to be a blood-borne infection transmitted through needles, blood transfusions and medical accidents, but not transmitted through sex. However, by 1989 we realised that while blood-borne infection is a real problem, sexual transmission of this virus is a *global* health hazard – with heterosexual infection probably outnumbering homosexual infection by two to one. There is a vaccine, but no cure.

Only some carriers become ill, with loss of appetite, tiredness, vomiting, fever and jaundice after an incubation period of several months. Hepatitis makes you feel very unwell. A proportion of those ill will go on to chronic hepatitis, with progressive liver failure, from which the majority may eventually die.[20]

It is easy to read a list like this and start to worry. If it is possible you have been exposed to STD infection, then you should go to a clinic for a check-up whether you have symptoms or not, but particularly if there is a discharge, soreness or discomfort around the genitalia.

You may read some of these lists and think you are infected – say with syphilis – when you are not. If in doubt, seek medical advice, remembering that a great number of infections that are *not* sexually transmitted can produce some of these symptoms. You cannot diagnose yourself.

You might think that the best way to avoid sexual diseases is to reduce the number of partners. However, life is not that simple. As we have seen, the commonest sexual pattern is serial monogamy, or faithfulness to one person at a time, but unfortunately this can be an ideal way to spread sex diseases. One partner infects another; and after a year, perhaps both have new partners, and infect one other person each. After another year or two, each of the four infects another. Eight becomes sixteen and so on. Therefore it is hardly surprising that even in the absence of what some would label 'promiscuous behaviour' (a loaded phrase, not mine), sexual diseases still spread.

The monogamy effect is particularly significant with AIDS. Unlike syphilis or gonorrhoea, where one exposure may well spread infection, HIV is relatively uninfectious. In the absence of other sexual diseases causing ulcerative damage to the surface of the genitalia, it *may* be that someone can have vaginal intercourse up to two hundred times on average without infection – the truth is that, as yet, we don't really know.[21] Many studies have looked at the risk of infection over time in couples where one is infected and the other not. Of course, the results vary greatly, because the infectivity differs from individual to individual.

HIV infection and AIDS

For example, the presence of other sexual disease can increase the risk of HIV infection up to seven times where there is ulceration,[22] while receptive anal intercourse probably doubles the risk.[23] Bleeding increases risk – for example, the rupture of the hymen in rape, or sex during menstruation. The level of virus in someone's body is very high for the first few weeks following infection and then falls, only rising again some years later as symptoms develop.

Someone having – say – ten one-night stands over ten months with unknown partners could be at far less risk than a faithful partner to someone infected, who is exposed to infection every time they have sex. Even if half the partners of the first person were infected with HIV, total exposure would be ten chances of 1 in 200 risk. Total risk of transmission would be 1 in 20. For the other person, the risk may be over 50 per cent. In Malawi, one in three women with HIV have been celibate, and then faithful to their husbands, yet infected because of their partner's previous history.[24]

The answer is to take HIV very seriously, recognising that sexual intercourse with a partner who could be infected will carry a significant risk – which is further increased when other factors are operating as well.

AIDS epidemic is no hype

There have been some very confusing reports in the British press recently, including odd claims that the AIDS epidemic in Africa is a myth, or even that HIV itself is perhaps harmless.[25] For a detailed view of the epidemic, see my book called *The Truth about AIDS*.[26]

Here is a very brief review based on results of thousands of research papers, talking to expert scientists at the very forefront of AIDS research, and my own experience as founder of a leading national and international AIDS agency operating in several different continents. It is also the view of the World Health Organisation and the overwhelming majority of European and American experts.

One in 250 of the entire adult population of the world is now thought to be HIV infected, with one new person added every 15 seconds.[27] Seven out of ten infections to date have been among heterosexuals, with nine out of ten of all new infections over the last year.[28] Once infection takes place, the person can be infectious, yet remain well, for many years – 15–20 years in some cases. Gradually, though, serious illnesses begin to develop as the immune system becomes damaged, leading to what we call AIDS. It seems that almost all with HIV will die of AIDS eventually, although – as with any slow-growing virus – people may die of other things in the meantime.[29]

In some towns and cities I have visited in Africa, the local people and governments estimate that up to a third of all sexually active men and women are carrying the virus.[30] In population after population, infection rates have soared, and wherever HIV has taken hold, death rates among the sexually active have risen correspondingly a few years later.

The evidence is overwhelming that HIV is lethal

It is true that you cannot categorically *prove* HIV leads to AIDS; any more than tobacco causes lung cancer. However, the evidence is overwhelming, and comes from hundreds of studies of disease in different populations.[31]

Here are a few examples: HIV enters the blood product supply for treating those with haemophilia. After a delay, the death rate among haemophiliacs rises. All these new deaths are pneumonias or other strange infections or cancers, destruction of the brain, skin problems and other things related to HIV. Those haemophiliacs testing negative for HIV remain well, while those testing positive become ill or die – and so do some of their spouses.

In Edinburgh in the mid-1980s, half of all drug injectors became infected with HIV in less than two years. Neighbouring Glasgow has far more drug users, but HIV reached the city later – in time to pay heed to the health warnings – so infection remained low. I have visited both cities many times, and helped to set up and support community-based care for those ill and dying. From what was known of numbers infected and when infection took place, we have been able to predict very accurately how many are likely to become ill with AIDS each year and to need care. Those predictions have been fulfilled, and while patterns of drug abuse are almost identical between the two cities, the AIDS cases in Glasgow are comparatively few and far between (despite the far larger drug community there).

In Africa, the evidence is just as obvious. For example, Dr Daan Mulder studied 9,400 inhabitants of 15 villages in south-west Uganda from 1989 to 1990. He found that young adults aged between 25 and 34 who tested positive for HIV were 60 times more likely to die within two years than those of the same age testing negative.[32] Death rates from tuberculosis and other illnesses associated with immune weakness have soared as HIV has spread.

Some reports suggested that malaria illness misled HIV tests, creating millions of false positives.[33] A moment's thought reveals the nonsense of this. Even if it is true, as some concede, that the earliest HIV tests ten years ago could be misread, an important fact remains: malaria has been a relatively constant feature of African life for years, yet something is changing. If the tests are simply responding to malaria, why the dramatic increase in HIV? There is another problem: HIV increases are also found in areas where malaria rates are low.

African problem hits Europe

There is also evidence closer to home. Even if we dismiss all the reports from those doctors from countries such as the United Kingdom who are serving overseas, and who predict a silent catastrophe from AIDS, there is also the direct evidence of our own eyes. In London, over six out of ten of all women with AIDS are Africans, mostly infected years before arrival.[34] Doctors and research workers have examined these men and women extensively. Their immune systems are shattered, yet their non-infected friends in this country are healthy. Many were ill shortly after arrival, and others have refused medication such as AZT, so it is illogical to blame other factors.

So where did they get HIV? In the back of a British Airways Jumbo Jet? All of them? What kind of mind can accept this kind of nonsense? Perhaps this is all an understandable denial of a very painful reality.

More US AIDS deaths each year than deaths during the Vietnam War

AIDS is real. Fifteen million are infected already, and the epidemic has hardly begun.[35] The first case was only diagnosed in 1981,[36] although we now have evidence of early infection in Africa (1960s),[37] America and Europe (1959).[38] In the United States there are probably at least 700,000 HIV carriers out of a total population of 255 million,[39] representing up to 1 in 60 of all men between the ages of 20 and 50.[40]

The Vietnam War killed 47,365 in battle, a war that dominated news bulletins for a decade and has scarred the memories of a generation.[41] It dominated my own childhood, and night after night I watched the news reports: more lost in combat, legs blown off by mines, ambushes in the jungle.

Yet more die every year in the United States of AIDS than died in the entire Vietnam War. In New York, AIDS is the commonest cause of death for men and women aged between 25 and 34, with a hundred AIDS deaths a week in 1994, and preparations are being made to care for 80,000 AIDS orphans by the year 2000.[42] Across the whole of the United States, one new person is infected every 13 minutes.[43]

The number already going to die in the United States as a result of existing HIV infection will be the equivalent of at least ten more Vietnam Wars. By as early as 1992, a total of 171,480 men, women and children had died.[44] The coffins from all those dead or dying in the future as a result of infection so far would stretch for up to 1,000 miles if laid out from end to end.

Terrible devastation in Africa

It is hard to convey in words the true extent of the terrible AIDS tragedy in Africa, which is overwhelming community after community as they struggle with their grief for thousands of loved ones. I have seen the devastation myself, and have helped the local people set up care programmes.

Public attention was caught recently by the appalling ethnic massacres in Rwanda: experts believe up to 500,000 perished in six weeks of 1994. Yet the death toll from AIDS in Rwanda, from those already HIV infected, will be vastly greater than the massacre itself, and every death leaves more children needing support. In Uganda, the death toll from AIDS from those already infected is likely to be more than three times the deaths through ethnic slaughter in Rwanda. The government says a total of at least 1.6 million were already infected by 1994.[45] Yet the death rates per thousand adults are even higher in some neighbouring countries, as are the numbers of reported cases – and Uganda is one of the countries most open about the problem.

Death rate figures can be gross underestimates due to under-reporting, but are helpful for comparison. In 1992, Uganda's death rate from AIDS per 100,000 people was 22, compared to 37 for Rwanda, 51 in Malawi, 36 in Kenya, and 79 in Zimbabwe.[46]

World Health Organisation surveys and other information were collated for Africa by the University of Natal in 1992 – figures accepted as trustworthy by the highly regarded Panos Institute in London. They give estimated levels of HIV infection among the sexually active as one in five for Malawi, 18–20 per cent for Zambia, 15–20 per cent for Zimbabwe, 8–10 per cent for Mozambique, 15–20 per cent for Angola, and so on.[47] The World Health Organisation says that 9 million were infected in total across sub-Saharan Africa by early 1994; and perhaps as many as 10 million children will have lost one or both parents because of AIDS by the year 2000.

A third of the truck drivers on the main trans-African highway are carrying HIV,[48] as are half the prostitutes or bar girls in many towns – possibly up to seven out of ten in some areas of south-west Uganda.[49]

Future disaster in South East Asia

At the World Health Organisation, the biggest worry of all is no longer the 9 million or more infected in Africa, but the pending disaster in South East Asia. Infection rates have leapt as rapidly as they did in Africa, particularly in countries like Thailand – which now has African levels of infection in some northern villages.[50]

Many dismiss Thailand as obvious and predictable because of its vast sex industry. However, India and other nearby countries appear to be going the same way – with possibly a million infected in India by 1994, according to the independent Indian Health Organisation. They are talking of a hundred new infections a day in Bombay alone, partly related to prostitution (a third of commercial sex workers are infected).[51]

The whole Asian subcontinent is beginning to experience the same kind of epidemic as Africa did several years ago. All the conditions are the same – partner exchange and other untreated sexual diseases. However, there is one vast difference: population. The number of sexually active adults in India alone exceeds the whole of sub-Saharan Africa. India alone could have more AIDS cases in a few years than the whole of Africa today. However, at least here we are aware and have time to prevent it. The African problem became severe before anyone realised what was going on, because the first deaths were blamed on other things.

The entire population of Africa was only 682 million in 1992, compared to 3.2 billion for Asia,[52] so infection in South East Asia is expected to dwarf that in Africa by the year 2000. Because HIV is a 'slow virus', with such a long incubation period, it may be a further decade before the full impact of illness and death is felt.

Then there is Latin America, now being hard hit, and also China and the countries of the former Eastern Bloc, sucking in great amounts of Western culture, lifestyles and disease.[53]

By 1993, the World Health Organisation calculated that the global social and economic costs of lost life were already in excess of $5,000 million, excluding all treatment and care costs.[54] I think this figure is very conservative, as we will see later.

Condoms alone cannot control AIDS

Many I talk to seem to assume that AIDS will just disappear into thin air if people are given enough condoms and told to use them. As we have seen, there are two big problems with this approach. Condoms are disliked by many, and they can be unreliable as contraceptives – with failure rates of 3–15 per cent per year for pregnancy,[55] and thus also a significant failure rate for HIV prevention.[56]

In 1991 and 1992, the World Health Organisation put out a statement to be used in nearly two hundred countries for World AIDS Day and throughout the year. It said: 'The most effective way to prevent sexual transmission of HIV is to abstain or for two people who are not infected to be faithful to one another. Alternatively the correct use of a condom will reduce the risk significantly.' In 1994, the UN year of the family, the statement was further strengthened to include the words 'abstinence and fidelity'.

In 1991, the US government said it was setting targets for the year 2000 to contain the explosive growth of AIDS and other STDs. The 'Healthy People 2000: National Health Promotion and Disease Prevention Objectives' reveal the massive scale of the problem.[57] They hope to keep new AIDS cases just below 100,000 each year,[58] at double the 1989 figures. They also aim to keep HIV levels below 800 people per 10,000, or around 1 in 100 of all adults. This, they say, will be an achievement. Furthermore, they plan to reduce the number of adolescents having sex, and to increase condom use by 15–19-year-olds from 26 per cent in 1988 to 60 per cent in the year 2000.

Similar goals were set by the British government in *Health for the Nation*,[59] which aimed to reduce gonorrhoea cases, numbers injecting drugs with shared equipment, and teenage pregnancy.

A post-AIDS world

We live in a post-AIDS world. Life after AIDS may continue, but culture will never be quite the same. AIDS will always be with us, unless a vaccine programme is developed that is as effective as that for smallpox. This is unlikely in the next 10 or 20 years, since we seem no nearer to finding a powerful vaccine today than we were five years ago, despite huge research efforts.[60] Fifteen experimental vaccines were tested between 1987 and 1993, with very little sign of success.[61]

Even if a one-dose low-cost cure is found, AIDS will continue to be part of our world, although less of a threat to affluent nations. Look at syphilis or TB: both have been fully treatable at relatively low cost for over half a century, yet we still have vast world epidemics of both today. In the meantime, drugs like AZT[62] are used to prolong life by a few months, but are very expensive and also toxic.[63]

More sex plagues from mega-cities

HIV was a terrifying mutation waiting to happen, and more may be coming. As the world population soars by 90 million each year, with each person alive there is another chance for an unlikely event. Viruses spread constantly between people, and less often between people and animals or the other way round.

By the year 2000, half the world's population of 6,000 million will be living in mega-cities. Every year, between

20 and 30 million are moving to urban areas in search of a better life. Most end up in slums with no water, electricity or sewers, few proper roads, and temporary housing for millions of people over hundreds of square miles, extending in every direction every day by the arrival of yet more people who start building homes on the outer edges.

By AD2000, cities like Bombay will have 25 million inhabitants, Mexico City 18 million, and Jakarta 17 million; 60 per cent in Asia may be living in mega-city slums. There has never been a time in human history when conditions have been so ideal for rapid mutation of new viruses, each able to spread rapidly through huge populations. In addition to all this, people are very worried about resources.[64]

Virus mutations are increasing. Ten or twenty years ago, medical students used to be shown typical skin rashes of illnesses such as measles or chickenpox. You were expected to recognise common illnesses the moment a child walked into the surgery. Today, hundreds of doctors scratch their heads as they look at sick children with various non-specific rashes, high temperatures and other symptoms. The same is happening in adults. Doctors often use such phrases as 'a self-limiting viral illness' – meaning they often have no idea what virus is causing it. What they really mean is that your child may be suffering from yet another viral mutation.

Viruses mutate every day

Every time a virus infects a single cell there is a chance that viruses made there will be different from that which actually went in. The reason that it is so hard to make a common cold vaccine is virus mutation: the virus adapts and changes, so by the time you have given your cold to your friends and they have jet-setted it around the world, the virus has changed, your immunity is useless, and you catch the same cold again.

However, HIV is one of the most chaotic and unstable viruses ever studied. In just one person over a period of months, you will find hundreds or even thousands of minor variants. That is one reason why HIV is almost completely immune to human antibodies. A major change has happened at least seven times with HIV, so we now have HIV-1-0, plus five types of HIV-1 and also HIV-2.[65] We have already seen what an easy life sex germs lead, therefore we can expect that AIDS will not be the last sexual disease to appear in the world.

If HIV produced death in months and not years, the consequences would have been unthinkable, although rapid death does slow down spread by reducing the numbers of those infected, yet unaware. What if a new serious viral illness spread by sex turned out to be almost as infectious as syphilis? This is very unlikely, but the point I am making is that sexual diseases are a real and increasing threat globally, and their impact has increased with AIDS. Even if HIV only spreads slowly in countries like the United Kingdom or Australia as a result of education and other STD treatment, the impact on the United States is likely to be great, and so much of world culture is drawn from here.

The AIDS generation

Teenagers today are the AIDS generation. They are growing up in a world where the chances of exposure during a one-night stand in many parts of the world is already up to one in three – or higher in the case of commercial sex workers. They are growing up in a world where conditions are set for catastrophe. Just consider the global impact of child prostitution on the lives of the children involved, and on the millions of sex tourists who every year travel thousands of miles to use and abuse them.

In Taiwan alone there are probably 60,000–200,000

child prostitutes, while UNESCO says that at least 800,000 children are working as prostitutes in Thailand – just two countries.[66] Up to a million children each year are sold as sex slaves in South East Asia, and very large numbers are becoming infected with a wide variety of sexual diseases – including HIV. AIDS will dominate many aspects of their adult lives, and the lives of their partners.

Then there is spread of HIV between adults. When India alone has 8 million infected, when 50 countries report levels as high as Thailand today, and air travel continues to boom, the impact will be considerable.

No country is immune

With one of the lowest HIV infection rates in Europe,[67] the British like to pretend that their country is protected by the fact that the sea separates them from other continents. Life insurance companies are not impressed, though. They tripled premiums for young men, and doubled them for women, at the height of the AIDS scare – this is now seen as an over-reaction, but insurance companies are still worried.[68] AIDS is a major risk for them, and they have not reduced their premiums.[69]

As we have seen in Eastern Europe, even walls of concrete, barbed wire, booby traps and bullets cannot prevent mass movements of people – and along with people travel the viruses. Since the collapse of communism, Eastern Europe has shown an explosion of interest in our ageing sexual revolution, discovering it for the first time. Drug addiction and HIV are spreading there too. Most of the 200 new European infections every day are thought to be in the eastern part.[70] Some of these have been spread through medical treatments. For example, a recent survey of 2,362 children in Romania found that 7.3 per cent were infected – almost all through contaminated needles used for medication. Spread is still occurring.[71] Up to one in ten children in orphanages were infected before the revolution in 1990, but a similar proportion are still infected today.

AIDS still has a 'gay plague and drug addict' image in many developed countries. However, the rate of increase among heterosexuals is rapid in both the United States and the United Kingdom. Many gay men have sex with women, and many infected drug users are sexually active. A large British study carried out by Birmingham University (1993) found that six out of ten gay men reported having sex with a woman,[72] and one US study found the figure to be one in four.[73] A British survey conducted by London University in 1993 reported seven out of ten drug injectors were sexually active, a similar proportion never used condoms with regular partners, and one in three never used condoms with casual partners – even if either of the two of them was known to be infected.[74]

In a world of civil wars, political upheavals, refugees, people seeking asylum, HIV infection can, and does, travel. What happens in Uganda will tend to happen in Malawi, what happens in Spain will tend to happen in France, and what happens throughout Europe will eventually affect Britain. It is true there will continue to be startling local differences, as we have already seen between Edinburgh and Glasgow, and even more so between neighbouring countries because of distinct cultures, customs and history. Yet the tendency for HIV infection to spread from highest-incidence nations to the lowest is obvious and already happening.

AIDS is a very unpleasant illness

As a doctor specialising in the care of the dying, I have cared for many people in the last days of their lives. Most of my earlier work was in supporting at home those with cancer – helping to relieve pain and other unpleasant symptoms. Then I discovered that three-quarters of the British AIDS problem was within a few miles of my

London home. I was then asked to help those with AIDS too, which led me to set up a new AIDS care and prevention organisation.

I often say that if I had to choose death between cancer and AIDS I would choose cancer. People are shocked, because the picture they have of cancer death is slow, painful and lingering. However, cancer pain is usually relatively easy to relieve, and so are most other cancer symptoms – thanks to excellent advances by the hospice movement that started in the United Kingdom.[75]

AIDS, though, is different. I am speaking from six years' experience in just one of the home-care teams I helped set up across the United Kingdom. This London team has cared for well over one thousand men, women and children in the last six years, with a holistic 'hospice' philosophy in the approach to care.

Most weeks I sit in the weekly meeting, where we discuss problems faced by those at home, and try to find new ways to help. We also ask those at home to score their own symptoms. Both our team meetings and client surveys confirm our anecdotal experience that those with AIDS often have severe symptoms that are very hard to relieve.[76]

Let me describe a few to you, mainly a result of a shattered immune system. Infection of the mouth and throat by thrush can be hard to treat, and can cause severe pain on swallowing; one person told me, 'It's like swallowing crushed glass', after trying to swallow small pieces of soft bread soaked in milk.

One in four AIDS patients may lose vision in one or both eyes, sometimes becoming completely blind. Many have memory loss, almost all experience crushing tiredness and weakness, many have severe diarrhoea from gut infections, or pain from shingles, genital herpes or other problems.[77]

Genital herpes is a real menace too. Even in healthy

individuals it is a painful nuisance, preventing sex when blisters erupt, but with AIDS the whole skin can begin to break down. I have seen a man at home with herpetic skin ulcers so deep on his backside that they exposed the bone. Losing control over the bowels or passing water involuntarily, unable to walk without falling, unable to remember who came to see you five minutes ago, nausea, vomiting, headaches, fevers, drenching night sweats . . . this is not a pleasant illness.

Some people say that you should hide all this; they say it will frighten people or depress them. But it is the truth; it is what many doctors and nurses are seeing every day. Some patients die of AIDS quickly with few of the above symptoms; but ironically, as treatment of other infections improves, we are seeing other more complex problems emerge quite commonly.[78] For example, someone may be completely well, unaware even that they have HIV, until they develop a sudden pneumonia, dying just a few days later. On the other hand, someone with HIV may first develop a number of vague medical problems; HIV is then diagnosed, preventative treatment for chest infections started, and they may survive for longer. Yet in such cases, things like loss of sight can become more common.

Every death has its impact on a new circle of people
Every AIDS death brings home the reality to a new circle of people. Someone I know in London has been to as many as fifteen funerals in one year. At each funeral there were other people for whom it was their first experience of AIDS. A Ugandan friend living in Kampala told me that most people he knew were attending an AIDS funeral once a month on average; and with each death, there may be children left behind. Many AIDS deaths are hidden, described to friends and family as cancer or pneumonia, with people taking their secret to the grave. Some of those

at AIDS funerals still think they have never been to one
– or even come across someone with the illness. This is
changing, though. One AIDS educator I know went into
three different schools one week recently in London. In
each, she was told of individuals who had AIDS known
to class members – things are becoming more open.

Early one Sunday morning about three years ago my
phone rang. It was a 24-hour news radio station: did I
know Freddie Mercury, lead singer with the group Queen,
had AIDS? Within an hour, I was in the studio. The
following morning at 6.30, I was rung again. Freddie had
died, and what did I think – people were saying he should
have told everyone the truth months ago instead of hiding
it. All that morning, people phoned in. I said I was glad
he had been open, even if it was late on in the illness. He
could have hidden the secret for ever; as it was, he had
helped make AIDS more real to some 100 million fans
across the world. My quote, 'Freddie's last gift to his fans',
became the headline on dozens of newspapers, both large
and small, right across the country. While some say that
Freddy Mercury's lifestyle made AIDS almost inevitable,
and that he was no role model for HIV prevention, the
point I am making is that every openly disclosed AIDS
death makes it easier for others to come forward.

Actors Rock Hudson (1985) and Ian Charleson (1990),
entertainer Liberace (1987), fashion designer Roy Halston
(1990), ballet dancer Rudolf Nureyev (1993), jazz musi-
cian Miles Davis (1991), model Tina Chow (1992), and
director Tony Richardson (1991) are just a few of the 2
million who have died so far.

As the infamous Stalin once said: 'One death is a
tragedy, a thousand deaths is just a statistic'. Every
death of one person is a loss to perhaps 10, 20, 30, 100,
200 or more people. Each has a ripple effect – yet another
personal and distressing reminder that sex can kill.

These are all reasons why I am convinced that sexual

diseases in general, and the recent plague of AIDS, will have a major increasing influence on the death of the old sexual revolution and on shaping the new revolution.

Cervical cancer – another cost of sex

Cervical cancer is another big health price to be paid for multiple sexual partners, killing 1,500 British women every year, with 15 new cases per 100,000. Cancer of the cervix (neck of the womb) is very rare in women who are virgins, but common in women with many partners – particularly if they started having sex when very young.[79]

Cervical screening was introduced in the 1960s, with a national programme introduced in 1988 that aimed to test all women between the ages of 20 and 60 every five years.[80] (Incidentally, as with every other illness linked to sex, it is possible to be affected even if monogamous for life, if *your partner* has had other partners.)

Cervical cancer is increasing, and is now one of the most common malignant diseases world-wide.[81] However, deaths are slowly falling in countries like the United Kingdom, with its programmes for earlier detection and treatment.[82] The cancer appears to be triggered by a number of different factors, which may or may not operate together. Most experts agree that one of the major factors is viral infection spread through sex.

Herpes simplex[83] and papilloma viruses have been implicated.[84] Some believe other risk factors may have an additional effect – for example, smoking,[85] folate deficiency (a vitamin present in normal diet),[86] and oral contraceptives.[87] The risk of cervical cancer is related to age at first intercourse[88] (the immature female cervix is especially prone to sexual infections), and the number of partners of the woman[89] or that her regular partner has had.[90] Condoms may be protective against this illness.[91]

Whether we look at cervical cancer, AIDS, or the many other illnesses related to sex, women tend to come out of it worse than men when it comes to sexual health. Fortunately, in most cases of these other illnesses, infection is obvious, superficial and diagnosed early.

When sex means no children

We have already seen that many sexual diseases can cause infertility, a problem causing intense suffering and distress to millions of couples, but often felt most by women.[92] Around one in six of all couples seek specialist help because of difficulty conceiving, and in 16 per cent there is a medical problem.[93] One in ten of all fertile couples will take more than a year to conceive, and one in twenty will take two.[94] However, one in twenty of *all* couples will never manage to conceive, despite all means of medical help. There are a wide range of reasons for infertility, including genetic factors, developmental abnormalities, effects of drugs used to fight cancers, damage of the reproductive organs, or cases where the cause is uncertain.

Some of the rise in infertility is because many couples are putting off pregnancy until they are in their thirties, when fertility is declining rapidly. This fact could well stabilise or slow down the increasing age at which people are now starting their families, unless new reproductive technology becomes widely used by women to have children after the menopause.

However, the commonest cause of infertility in women is pelvic inflammatory disease (PID). As we have seen, PID can be caused by a number of different sexually transmitted infections; and abortion has added to the PID problem because the procedure can also introduce infection. With each new infection of the fallopian tubes (salpingitis), they become more scarred, so they are no longer able to carry an egg from ovary to uterus.

Sexual disease can mean death from pregnancy

Pelvic inflammatory disease can kill. Every year a busy general hospital can expect to see a number of women admitted as acute emergencies with severe right- or left-sided abdominal pain. A common cause is a fertilised egg stuck in the tube – which is wide enough for sperm, but too distorted for an egg to travel along, as a direct result of previous PID. The developing embryo burrows into the delicate tube wall as if it were a thick muscular uterus. In such an ectopic pregnancy, the placenta forms in the wrong place, eroding big blood vessels in the process. Massive internal bleeding can result, with severe pain, internal haemorrhage, shock and death.

Fortunately, such an outcome from PID is rare. What is far more common is complete tube obstruction: sterilisation by infection. Surgeons specialising in tubal repair are much in demand, but the success rate is only 50 per cent, even where there is minimal damage,[95] while for others the likelihood of pregnancy afterwards is less than 20 per cent.[96]

Methods used for treatment vary with the reason for infertility; however, the process itself is often very stressful and the strain can get worse as treatment continues.[97] If the woman is ovulating normally and the man is producing viable sperm, the stage is set for IVF (in-vitro fertilisation). This is where sperm and eggs are mixed in the laboratory to allow fertilisation to occur, before placing a developing ball of cells inside the womb. This is a growth industry: 20 per cent more treatments every year in Britain,[98] – again largely due to the growth of PID-related infertility and medical advances in treatment.

Designer babies, cloning and foetal eggs

Rising infertility, much of it related to sexually transmitted diseases, has been the reason that so much effort has been put into reproductive technology, and the reason why it is so much in the news: designer babies, babies from foetuses, or cloning of embryos by artificial twinning, for example.[99]

At the Royal Society of Medicine, I recently took part in a debate with Professor Robert Edwards, creator – together with Patrick Steptoe – of the world's first test-tube baby in 1977, born in 1978. The question was how far we should go in reproductive techniques to help infertile couples have children, a question drawn into sharper focus by the increasing numbers of women with PID.

While very few would object today to using a couple's own sperm and eggs to produce their own genetic child, many are worried about other possibilities – for example, removing up to 5 million potential eggs from a single aborted female foetus,[100] used to give to women who have no functioning ovaries,[101] or choosing the sex of a child.[102]

Twinning (cloning) of human embryos is now possible following progress made by Dr Jerry Hall and his colleagues at George Washington University,[103] possibly preceded by others in Britain.[104] Techniques for freezing one twin embryo and growing the other to a baby are well established,[105] and time-warp twins have already been born.[106] Twinning imitates nature – over 4,000 identical healthy twins are born world-wide every day.[107] Artificial twinning could permit parents to choose a frozen embryo with known pedigree, by studying the older twin: height, weight, sex, intelligence, hair colour and many other factors could be predicted with some confidence.

You could implant the frozen twin embryo in a surrogate to produce spare parts for the older brother or sister – an option seriously suggested as possibly acceptable in some circumstances by Baroness Warnock, widely regarded as the custodian of the British conscience on matters relating to embryos.[108] One US clinic is ready to offer cloning commercially as soon as it is declared safe.[109]

Surrogacy is nothing new, although it raises important emotional and ethical issues, and is illegal on a commercial basis in Britain. A former leading campaigner for surrogacy, herself a surrogate mother, now says she feels it was a mistake to give away the child after birth to its genetic parents.[110]

These issues are all part of the heart-breaking problem of infertility, another cost of a sexual revolution that has failed to deliver.

Desperate struggle for healthy babies

Those who work in this field will tell you of the appalling stress and suffering caused by childlessness. Feelings of blame, guilt, lack of self-worth, loss of self-respect – enough to ruin many a sex life and many a happy stable relationship. Miscarriages can also produce great emotional suffering.[111]

While there are serious concerns about the abuse of reproductive technology, one thing is clear. The scientists and doctors involved are driven by the passionate desires of the people they are treating, people whose energies are focused on the thought of children of their own. Of course, there is also the fascination of the challenge to technology.

It is ironic that such increasing infertility should occur at the same time as a baby famine. More and more couples are desperately looking to adopt fewer and fewer available babies.[112] In Britain, the numbers of adoptions fell from 23,000 a year in 1974 to only 6,500 by 1990, while demand has grown.[113] One reason is that unwanted babies are becoming a thing of the past, with more people having abortions if they are unhappy about being pregnant. Another reason is that mothers may feel more able to keep babies in a world increasingly tolerant of single parenting.

It is common for couples to wait until their early thirties before trying for a family, then a year or two may elapse before they realise something is wrong and they seek treatment. Only when treatment fails do many think seriously about adoption, but there is often a wait for up to ten years. The child who arrives may be two to four years old, and they may have to wait a long time for a second. That is one reason why there is a growing black market in babies for sale in some countries.

In conclusion, sexual ill health, and its increasing contribution to a decline in fertility, are big issues in a post-AIDS world, and will increasingly be so. In an age more health-obsessed and green-oriented than any other, it is inevitable that these concerns will help shape a new sexual culture. The fact is that sex can be very damaging to your health; your next partner could be a serious health hazard.

I want to turn now from the medical consequences of the sexual revolution to the psychological ones. I want to look particularly at how many people's lives have been shattered emotionally by sexual chaos and the break-up of relationships.

5

PAIN OF PARTING

The health hazards of the sexual revolution are one thing, but what about emotional health and emotional pain? The impression has been given that in a world celebrating sexual freedom, so long as you take care about AIDS and other sexually transmitted disease there is nothing else to worry about. Emotional trauma is ignored.

This has been called the age of the 'dinkies' (dual income, no kids, easy divorce).[1] In Britain, this lifestyle was encouraged by the 1984 Matrimonial and Family Proceedings Act,[2] with 10 per cent of all marriages subsequently ending within two years[3] – but is life that simple? Not according to the agony columns, which are attempting to give out a lot more than sex advice. They try to help people cope with 'relationship pain', the true agony of their situations.

We have seen that the search for love is one of the most fundamental of human drives, influencing almost all other behaviour; and it is a search that can affect sexual behaviour.

We need to look now at what happens when people feel they have found the answer to that search – and then lose it. Bereavement following partner death is often deeply traumatic.[4] By the age of 65, one in five married men have lost their wives through death, and half of all women are widowed.[5] Those at most risk emotionally are those who are young with several children, a previously happy marriage, and now find themselves in financial difficulties.[6]

However, we are going to turn next to grief caused by partner separation, its long-term effects, and what we know about predicting long-term stability and happiness. My purpose is to show that sexual freedom without emotional trauma is a myth for many. Having a number of different partners is not a mere sexual adventure, but has huge consequences in many cases in terms of depression and heartache. However, as we will see, recent research is helping us understand the elusive secrets of longer-term happiness.

Grieving after separation is complicated by conflicting emotions, and the fact that both partners are still alive. Their paths may cross and re-cross with shared friends, neighbourhood or places of work. The chances of a 'clean break' drop almost to zero if children are involved. Every time the divorced or separated parent looks at his or her children, there are powerful reminders of the previous partner – in their very existence and 'family likeness'.

Women are often more dissatisfied than men

Although living together outside of marriage is common, most research on partner happiness has been done on those who get married. The divorce statistics are ghastly, with one divorce for every two marriages in Britain in 1992 – many of the divorces of people already divorced at least once before.[7] Three out of four of all divorces are initiated by women, and women are generally more dissatisfied by marriage than men.[8] One sex therapist said recently that, in his experience, a great many women in middle years were bored with the lack of emotional response from their husbands, and ended up by seeking more support from other women – although their partners usually had no idea that anything was wrong.[9]

If we were to extend the trends from 1971 to 1991 on to 2011, we might find that divorces had equalled marriages by then. However, this is very unlikely because of the changes already coming. As we have seen, it is still true that *most* marriages last for life at the moment. Despite gloomy predictions by the UK Family Policy Group of a 40 per cent divorce rate for new marriages by the year 2000,[10] there are signs of a flattening out of the massive jump in divorces and the plummeting marriage rates.

The British divorce rate doubled from around 80,000 divorces per year in 1971 to 157,000 within ten years. However, the rate only rose to 170,000 at the end of another decade, while the marriage rate from 1981 to 1991 hovered around or near the 375,000 mark.[11]

We have already seen that three times as many adults in the United Kingdom in 1993 wanted divorce to be made harder than wanted the law to be eased.[12] At the same time, more and more couples are looking for professional help. Relate saw only 22,000 people in 1971, but the figure had risen to 70,000 by 1991, and 76,000 two years later.[13]

You cannot have love without grief

Recently, I sat on the Bench with a County Court judge as he deliberated over case after case of partner dispute. Wrangles over housing, property, income – and children. Who looks after them? Where should they live? Can Dad take them out for a day? An hour? At all?

You cannot have love without grief. The more the love, the greater the pain of separation – from whatever cause. And at a time of great loss, there is often isolation. One study of divorced women in the United States found that they often lost a wide circle of friends, although closest family and friends kept in touch. Families tended to rally round divorced mothers with pre-school children, but such mothers often had unmet needs – ranging from lack of emotional support, to financial difficulties, need for a boyfriend, partner or spouse, time for themselves and for child care.[14]

Single-parent mothers on low incomes are most likely to be sad and unhappy. Six out of ten in a study of 225 women were found to be very depressed, affecting not only their own emotional health, but also their attitudes to their children. This in turn affected their children's behaviour.[15] As we have already seen, one Norwegian study discovered that divorced or separated people have a four times greater chance of needing admission to a psychiatric ward compared to those married.[16]

A particularly vulnerable time for single parents can be when their children grow up and leave home. This is a big adjustment for all parents, but at least parents together have each other. Coping with the empty nest can be far more difficult on your own, especially when older teenagers have been providing a substitute for a partner's company.[17]

Divorce increases poverty

According to Dr Angela Dale, deputy director of the Social Science Research Unit at City University, London, a new female underclass is being created by single parenting, of which a large element is due to marital breakdown. She looked at 11,500 men and women aged 33 in 1991, and found that single mothers were often 'hard up, having lost their hold on the job market, and faced every prospect of an impoverished old age dependent solely on state pensions. They were trapped in a downward economic spiral in which the demands of bringing up a child single-handedly cut income.'[18]

If divorce is so destructive, then we need to look at ways to prevent it. Attitudes towards a relationship by both people is a key to the future of the relationship – cynicism is likely to wreck it before it starts. The trouble is that previous hurts can make people feel very cautious about how much they trust or are willing to invest. Trauma in one generation can lead to relationship neglect in another, and a cycle of unhappiness may repeat itself – as research has shown.[19]

One response has been to take out insurance against divorce,[20] or pre-marriage settlements. You go to a solicitor before you get married to agree divorce terms in advance – just in case. Such arrangements, though, are unlikely to lead to happier or more stable marriages. Research suggests we will find the opposite, because anything that undermines the strength of long-term commitment to work things out is likely to encourage a split.

An easier exit may make life harder

I remember one female medical student I trained with who got married and decided to keep her maiden name. That is a valid decision for many reasons – for example, equal recognition of women rather than negating female identity and lineage in male paternalism. However, this particular young woman said that her motivation was insecurity, because her own parents had split up and she had little confidence in her own marriage. She did not want the hassle of changing her professional name if she divorced. In fact, she was separated in less than twelve months, and divorced within two years. I am *not* saying here that the marriage would have worked better if she had changed her name. You may feel that women changing their names after marriage is oppressive, and why should women bear yet another unequal cost of divorce? What I *am* saying, though, is that research shows that you tend to get out what you put in.[21] Attitudes count: they shape our responses to each other, communication, and even our sex lives.

Feeling secure is very important in long-term, happy relationships, where each person feels able to rely on the other, and partners are 'psychologically available' – in other words, they are 'around' and really listening to each other.[22] The feeling of mutual dependence in a satisfying and close relationship is one of the most deeply rewarding human experiences – far more likely to sustain a lifetime marriage than sex alone. Security means couples can laugh at themselves, and keep a sense of proportion at times of tension.[23]

So why do people get into relationships that are likely to destroy them, their partners and possibly their children? Is love so blind? How can we help people see trouble ahead before they get married rather than eight weeks after?

We need to learn from others' mistakes

Perhaps every couple preparing to get married tends to look around for a role model: a relationship that is happy and fulfilling, where both people treat each other well, and are discovering their full potential. We all have our own explanations and theories as to why Mark and Claire broke up, or why David and Mary are so happy, or why we reckon Jane and Stephen will split up within a year. We apply these anecdotal experiences to our own lives and the lives of our children – and try to learn from other people's experience.

But what does research show? First, I want to look at long-term relationships and at attempts to predict survivors out of those already partnered. Secondly, I want to look at partner selection. These things are vitally important to the whole future of sexual behaviour. If it becomes clear that we now know how to help guarantee that a marriage will be happy long term, how to select an ideal partner, and how to work it out together, it may lead to a new confidence and belief in stable relationships. As we have seen, when people fall in love, most do want to believe it could last for ever. Yet what is the evidence that it can?

New research helps long-term happiness

There are few great surprises from all the studies: love, care, affection, unselfishness, agreement, consensus, understanding,[24] a willingness to listen, be flexible, give, apologise, make adjustments and spend time talking together are all important.[25] Research shows that despite popular fiction, spouses do not *become* more similar with years of marriage – many are similar *before* they get married,[26] although similarity is not necessarily a predictor of happiness, as we will see.

Verbal or physical abuse, lack of respect for the other, drug or alcohol addiction,[27] unwillingness to invest time and effort in communication or in resolving difficulties, taking the other person for granted, long-standing hostility, unwillingness to apologise, rigidity and unwillingness to make adjustments are all factors associated with risk of marital breakdown.

Marriages can also come under pressure when children arrive, partly because of the change from a simple partnership to a family unit. One in three couples in a recent British survey said their relationship declined as a result of increased conflict after the birth of their first child. However, those relationships that survived seemed to have a good foundation for the future.[28] The answer is for both partners to be particularly sensitive to the other's needs at that time of change, to keep talking, making each other continue to feel important and special. The arrival of a child is very often a time of great happiness and celebration for both, further strengthening a lifelong relationship with a new sense of purpose together.

For Sheila and I, having children has been a wonderful experience, a never-ending source of enrichment and pleasure. Of course, it can also be tiring and emotionally taxing at times, especially when it comes to loss of sleep with a baby, the feeling of utter responsibility for a newborn child, and, later on, the issues of discipline – with the inevitable clash of wills and personalities.

We waited several years after being married before we had children, enjoying being able to pursue two full-time careers without time conflicts, and enjoying the freedom. When children came, we were both ready and looking forward to it; it was something we wanted to do together, an important new development in our relationship. Incidentally, we got married relatively young – at 21 and 22 – and waited until then to begin a sexual relationship, which for each of us was our first. Therefore our wedding day was vitally significant, the start of the whole of the rest of our lives, a celebration of coming together. 'Life after sex' for us has been life after making a public commitment to care for and be faithful to each other. Our entire intimate language of erotic love has been built with each other over the years, and every time we enjoy sex, we do so as a powerful, passionate experience of that same declaration, commitment, affection and security.

Predicting divorce

The number of studies using different factors to try and predict long-term marriage stability is growing rapidly[29] – a whole new research industry.[30] We know enough now for a bookmaker to be able to offer stakes on the likelihood of an engaged couple still being together for their golden wedding (50 years).

Since the average length of marriage before separation can be as little as five years, it is obvious that many relationship problems have their roots in the pre-marital stage. As we have seen, in many cases the process of breaking up has started less than a year after marriage. Therefore the nature of pre-marriage relationships should be a good indicator of what is to come[31] – except in arranged marriages, where the indicators are likely to be other equally predictable factors. Incidentally, there are many negative comments about arranged marriages, but where the choice has been a good one, with some involvement of the two concerned, the result can often be an affectionate, caring, lifelong relationship. After all, as we have seen, many people left entirely to make their own choices make disastrous decisions.

We have seen that divorce in one generation makes divorce more likely in the next, although the added risk is relatively small.[32] Teenagers from divorced families go out on dates more often, and are less happy in their pre-marriage relationships than others,[33] particularly if divorce is associated with hostility between parents, conflict between the parents and the child, and if the parent retaining custody remains single.[34]

It is well known that teenage marriage is a high risk.[35] However, if you survive the first five years, the risk falls towards the average for all marriages.[36] Marriage after the age of 30 also carries a higher risk factor, because adjustment gets more difficult with age.[37] So the lowest age risk is for couples getting married in their twenties.

Look before you leap

Longer courtship makes happy marriage more likely,[38] probably because there is increased time for adjustment.[39] However, *very* long courtship before marriage, including cohabitation with varying degrees of enthusiasm for getting married, is more likely to end in eventual divorce.[40]

I can remember someone once saying they would be engaged for seven years. If they can wait that long without any urgent feelings to be 'one', what kind of glue is going to hold them together? If they are going to live together anyway as man and wife beforehand, but with a private commitment to each other, why not do it publicly and celebrate a great start to the most important human relationship in their lives? Some live together because they say they need to save up for various things, but possessions and income on their own don't make happy marriages. The strongest foundation is found somewhere else.

The other factors making lifelong marriage more likely are happiness in parents' marriages, a warm relationship with parents and brothers or sisters, low levels of childhood conflict with parents, and a background of firm parental discipline.[41] 'Tranquillity, frankness and steadiness' in men and 'frankness, stability and contentedness' in women are low-risk factors for divorce – so are 'consideration for others, companiableness, self-confidence and emotional dependency on the other, having the same degree of attractiveness, or extraversion or intelligence'.[42] Emotional dependency is a positive thing when both partners feel it towards each other, because it binds them together. They feel they need each other in order to be happy in an exclusive, emotionally fulfilling attachment, and they want to share their lives deeply.

On the other hand, constant arguments before marriage, tension and conflict, physical aggression or communication problems are predictors of a likely weak relationship, with serious problems developing two or more years later.[43] Burgess and Wallin carried out a classic study of 1,000 engaged couples in 1953. Broken engagements were associated with parental disapproval, differences in leisure time preferences or religious faith, lower levels of expressed affection, and less confidence in the happiness of their future marriage.[44]

Deception, avoiding talk about the relationship, and conflict all erode relationships in early stages. The trouble is we tend to be less accurate in detecting deception the longer relationships last.[45] The most damaging area of deception is a secret relationship with someone other than your partner. It does not even need to be the act of sex;

there is also such a thing as *emotional* adultery, which can rob a partner of intimacy and knowledge.

Computer-assisted predictions

Attempts have been made to combine all these things into score sheets – such as 'PREPARE', which measures 11 risk factors to predict relationship survival. It looks at realistic expectations, personality issues, communication, conflict resolution, financial management, leisure activities, sexual relationship, children and marriage, family and friends, egalitarian roles and religious orientation. It is useful for predicting who is most likely to be happy or unhappy, divorced or not, but the limits of its accuracy are not much more than three years after marriage.[46]

So, then, there is hope for people who are fed up with relationships that don't work. Choose the person you invest your life in with great care (perhaps taking into account the opinions of good friends and family as people more likely to be objective), develop the relationship slowly in a loving and unselfish way, and keep making the relationship a priority for the rest of your lives – and make sure the person you love feels the same way about you, and has similar expectations, before you get too involved. You don't *have* to get divorced – most people don't. Of course, both spouses need to be equally committed to making things work.

So often, people start going out with someone they are initially attracted to, without much thought, and end up getting married, then divorced. Can we wind back the video-tape to see what is going wrong? I have lost count of all the times that Sheila and I have heard people tell us that they would never consider marrying the person they are going out with 'because it would never work'. So what were they doing? Just playing at relationships?

Even short-term relationship break-up is often traumatic, especially if they have had sex together.

We have seen over and over again how people get more and more drawn into disastrous relationships. They start going out with someone they know could be a big risk long term, but is fun to be with now, and then they begin to fall in love and lose objectivity. 'Love at first sight' can be particularly suicidal: an instant and overwhelming infatuation with a near-total stranger. Sometimes it works out, but very often it doesn't. The second or third date with someone very attractive may be the last completely objective decision you make about that relationship. We need to think carefully from a distance before losing our hearts to an uncertain future if we want to increase our chances of long-term happiness. If not, we may find ourselves propelled against common sense into long-term misery, from which the trauma of later divorce comes as a relief.

Compatible, or just a good relationship?

Over the last seven decades, theories have come and gone about whom we choose as partners and why. Freud told us we tended to marry people who unconsciously reminded us of our opposite-sex parent.

Then came 'compatibility' theories: if various aspects of our personalities and backgrounds match, then the theory was that we should get on well. This is the 'birds of a feather flock together' folklore, and initially it seems as if research backs this up.

Many studies have found that couples tend to be similar in attitudes and values, personality, physical attractiveness, age, sex, religion, race and other things. However, part of this could be because we tend to move in certain circles of friends because of where we are brought up, and hence this may narrow our choices. Similarity, though, does *not* predict who stays together and who breaks up.[47] Another version of 'compatibility' theory is that 'opposites attract': we choose people who will complement who we are. This is widely believed, but again there is little science to back it up.[48]

Most work on relationships has turned away from these simplistic explanations of background or personality to look at how people relate to each other. What happens when two people spend time together? How do they communicate? How do they behave? Do they have positive attitudes to each other? What is the quality of the relationship? Is there any commitment to work things out? Do they love each other?[49] Of course, similarity can help these things, for example if interests are shared, or two people have a similar educational background, or come from similar family culture. These courtship studies are fascinating, and once the media wakes up to them I believe we will begin to see a profound effect on partner choice and behaviour, with improved relationship stability. After all, who wants to be miserable when you can be happy for life?

This information makes it more likely that those who want to will be able to build long-term relationships with a realistic expectation based on the positive and negative experience of tens of thousands of others. With care and attention they know their relationships are likely to bring lasting pleasure and be a deeply enriching experience.

The alternatives are not glamorous; they are bleak. Flitting around from one person to another may be acceptable to many 20-year-olds, but when you are in your late thirties or early forties, questions about whether you will ever have a family can start to grow, especially for women, or doubts about whether you want your current partner to be the father or mother of any children you may have.

Painful reality of approaching middle age

A friend recently went to a school reunion. Some people were still single, and very happy and fulfilled to be so. Many others were married and had 'settled down', often with a number of children who were fast growing up. Others were in various kinds of sexual relationships.

One former classmate said she now had a 'live-in weekend partner', a relationship of temporary companionship and convenience. However, the reality is that at the age of 38 her fertility is now falling rapidly, and the possible medical complications of pregnancy and birth are increasing all the time. If she wants to have children of her own, time is fast running out. Many men who want children have 'settled down' by the age of 40, while others may have no desire for long-term ties. A divorced man may have children of his own already. These are painful issues with no easy answers especially when some women – or indeed men – may feel their choices are limited.

One decade on, the philosophy of transience becomes even harder to cope with: a 48-year-old woman married at the age of 20, now divorced with two teenage children. A 50-year-old man living alone in a bedsit, paying mainten- ance to keep his ex-wife and three children in the family home – just one of 25 per cent of British households, a threefold increase in single living from 1961 to 1992.[50] Part of this is due to death of spouses in an ageing population, but a significant element is because of the breakdown of long-term relationships as part of the sexual revolution.

Or a man who has had five relationships, each lasting several years, now alone again at 48, wondering what will happen when he is 60. This is the dry, harsh reality. The debris of youthful hopes, years and shattered dreams.

What life can be like after sex

A 46-year-old woman has two children from different fathers; these children don't get on. Her male lodger has become a sexual partner, resented by her 17-year-old, who is moving out. The eight-year-old cries every night for his dad. He is withdrawn, and his teacher is concerned. He is scared of the lodger. His own dad has another woman now. His new step-mum is 24 and has just had a baby – no time for him. You will find similar or more complicated situations in any school or in the law courts. Children may need protecting.[51]

Transience becomes more and more costly as the years pass. A man in his sixties starts another relationship with a married woman, and tries to persuade her to leave her husband. The relationship is discovered, and the wife leaves to live with the man, but finds him difficult. She separates, now facing 30 years of decline towards old age on her own. Her children have never forgiven her.

Such things may make powerful subjects for plays, films and books, but they can be hell to live through.

A generation to judge

The trouble with social experiments is that they usually take a generation or two to assess. What happens to a nation pulverised by the biggest divorce rate in history and the biggest rate of cohabitation and births outside marriage? No one knows, but the impact is likely to be almost immeasurably large on every aspect of life well into the middle of the next century. Will there be a reaction when we count the cost? Of course there will – there is already.

All is not lost if people hit problems in their marriages. Marital therapy is a boom industry, offering hope in distress, whether through agencies like Relate, psychotherapy-based models or other sources.[52] Relate's income in 1992–3 was almost £10 million.[53] Why the boom? Because so many people are facing the collapse of their relationships, and realise how much trauma it will involve to separate. Deep down, they hope there is a better way forward. They want to believe there can be hope.

So what approaches are being taken? These hardly fill newspaper or magazine pages yet, but are a mark of a trend to come. This is important, because every new understanding we have of how to make relationships in difficulties work long term, brings nearer the romantic ideal for more people.

Preventing marital distress

It is possible to categorise behaviour of couples into different kinds of relationship patterns, depending on how they tend to resolve conflicts, avoid them, or escalate them, in another method of predicting divorce risk.[54]

Researchers at the University of Denver in Colorado have been following up couples over five years of therapy designed to teach them how to improve communication and work through conflict. After five years, communication in many had improved significantly, and levels of violence had fallen.[55] Thus marital therapy helps prevent divorce and conflict.

Violence by husbands is a common problem, and you can predict in advance those marriages where it is more likely to happen. Domestic violence is more likely in relationships where the husband is subordinate, with less earning power, less decision-making power, and poorer communication skills. It has been suggested (without wanting to try and justify violent behaviour in any form) that violence by husbands may sometimes be compensatory behaviour to make up for perceived lack of power in other areas of the marriage. If this is the case, marital therapy can be directed, among other things, at helping to restore a man's self-image as well as directly encouraging self-control and conflict resolution in non-violent ways.[56] Some models of family therapy tend to play down the seriousness of violence by emphasising shared responsibility for whatever happens. A worrying survey of 362 therapists in the United States found that very few took much notice of violence and the need for protection of wives.[57]

In a world that is still strongly male-dominated and paternalistic, some marriages get into added difficulties when roles are altered.[58] For example, a married woman going out to work for the first time after years of staying at home may enjoy extra income and financial independence; she may also do less domestic chores, with her husband expected to take a more equal share. One study in New Jersey suggests that these changes may be beneficial for women, but that the mental health of some husbands can be affected by the stress of the adjustment.[59] We need to see marriage in the context of the whole of life, helping partners to release each other to their full potential, adjusting to change without feeling trapped or threatened.

Many couples get 'stuck' in conflict, expecting the other to make the first move, the first apology. My experience is that when you think an apology is due but not forthcoming, look in your own heart for something you can apologise for yourself and take the initiative to apologise first. As that happens, it often triggers a corresponding response, helping break down the wall of mutual hostility and resentment.[60] If that fails, and there seems to be deadlock, then outside help may be needed – from a mutual trusted friend or perhaps a professional counsellor.

Alcohol abuse and marriage
Alcohol abuse is a common cause of marital distress, and urgent attention needs to be given to combating this

problem at individual, local and government levels.[61] An existing alcohol problem can also be made worse by an unhappy marriage.[62]

Parental alcohol abuse affects children in many ways. A study of 16,795 adults in the United States aged between 18 and 39 found that white adults were 50 per cent more likely to get married early if a parent abused alcohol, which may help explain why so many of the marriages of children from 'alcoholic' homes break up; youth is a big risk factor in marital breakdown.[63] Marriages may take place early because older teenagers are trying to escape alcohol-related problems at home, or because they have a greater need than other teenagers for love and affection.

Midlife changes can spell trouble

Sometimes marriages can hit problems just when pressures seem to be easing. A large number of couples seek professional help during midlife changes.[64] Some of these couples have long-standing problems, but others have marriages that seem at first sight to be highly successful. They are more financially secure, more established professionally and socially, less controlled by the demands of young children, yet still in deep trouble.

Lifelong marriage can only happen by constant adaptation to changes within each person in the relationship; yet those same changes can help to keep a relationship fresh and interesting. It is obvious that change has taken place with the birth of a child or a new job, yet change is happening continually. People who just *hope* to 'live happily ever after' are likely to find, years later, that they are married to a stranger – if still married at all.[65]

Which couples respond best to help?

Can you predict who will be helped most by marital

therapy or marriage guidance counselling? An important report from the Department of Psychology at Texas University suggests that you can. Three psychologists looked back at how 55 couples had progressed over four years. Those couples most likely to be divorced or still very unhappy were the ones where at the start of the counselling one partner was very depressed, where there were poor problem-solving or communication skills, and where one or both were unskilled workers.[66] It seems that you need a certain level of intelligence and emotional commitment to get the best out of some of these approaches.

Many difficulties can be caused or made worse by health problems.[67] Doctors and nurses are often very slow to recognise this or discuss it – for example, with sex and heart disease problems,[68] gynaecological cancers[69] or Alzheimer's disease.[70]

On the other hand, helping people's marriages can improve health – or the partners' ability to live with illness. For example, marital therapy has often been used for couples where one or other has severe chronic low back pain. In Finland, 63 couples were found where chronic back pain was a problem, and half of them were given marital therapy. After five monthly sessions with two therapists, they were all followed up a year later. It was found that communication improved in the treated group, and worsened in the control group (no therapy). Levels of psychological distress were less with treatment,[71] although the actual disability remained the same.[72]

Helping couples resolve conflict may reduce blood pressure in men, which can shoot up when they try to influence or control their wives,[73] and reduce depression or suicide rates among women – because suicide is not unusual in severe cases of marital distress in the absence of professional help.[74] Marital therapy can be a very effective way to treat some people with depression, by dealing with the main cause of distress.[75]

Family doctors are well placed to help couples with relationship or sexual difficulties. They may have known the partners and their children for years, and built up trust. This 'therapeutic alliance' is vital for success in supporting a couple through painful adjustment.[76] With training, many doctors can more easily help identify those couples who are heading for a crisis and offer them support.[77]

Sex problems can emerge in long-term relationships

As we have seen, sexual dissatisfaction or dysfunction is very common, affecting perhaps onc in five of all adults at any time,[78] including the elderly.[79] We have already seen how our culture creates sexual dissatisfaction, even where there was none before, by stressing a sexual ideal that is based on fantasy rather than reality. 'Sensation-seeking' does not guarantee fulfilment. Indeed, the opposite may be true. One study found that female 'sensation-seekers' had greater sexual desire, greater sexual arousal and more positive attitudes towards sex, but had the same frequency of sexual intercourse and greater marital or sexual dissatisfaction.[80]

When people think of sex problems, they often think of impotence, premature ejaculation or lack of orgasm in women. While great progress has been made in treating impotence with medication, and premature ejaculation with stop-start techniques,[81] most sexual difficulties such as impotence or lack of orgasm are caused by psychological and emotional factors (as well as physical ones such as poor technique).[82] Dr Paul Brown is a psychiatrist who set up one of Britain's first government-funded sex clinics. In four out of five cases it is women who seek him out, hoping their partners will follow. Dr Brown often asks couples how they make 'intimate time' for one another. He said, 'In so many marriages, sex stops being something for which time is created. It's a kind of quick relief function. Who would do anything for *real* pleasure in the last fifteen minutes before falling asleep?'[83]

Sex therapy growing

As with marital therapy,[84] there are many different sex therapy approaches. All appear to help some people, but others are not helped, and it is hard to choose one method on the basis of results.[85] Sex therapy has a useful place in supporting some marriages. While it is true that the demand for it has perhaps been increased by the sexual revolution itself, genuine difficulties exist and people need help.

A deciding factor on which approach to take will be cultural. For example, different strands of Asian traditions can be used in sexual counselling of people from a Hindu or Buddhist background in a way totally different from an approach for devout Muslims or Christians.[86] An approach to a couple from an ethnic minority in Britain might be very different from a couple in India, Malawi or Thailand.

Common reasons for sexual difficulties are negative, confusing, guilt-inducing or traumatic sexual experiences. While sexual abuse has been increasing, so have the casualties. One successful approach for those who have been abused has been to help the person to be a 'survivor' rather than a 'victim'; this means helping a couple to develop a very fulfilling sex life, for this then stops the abuse from controlling the present and the future as well as the past.[87]

The aim of therapy is not just to restore a sex life, but to create a 'style' of sexual behaviour together that draws the relationship closer, strengthening, enriching and energising it in every way.[88] After initial meetings with a therapist, best results are obtained if couples return for follow-up every six months. They usually need to find regular time together to enjoy giving each other intimate, physical pleasure without all the pressures of intercourse, having agreed to set themselves realistic goals.[89]

Attempts have been made to try and combine marital and sex therapy sessions in group sessions,[90] or with just a couple on their own.[91] Clearly, the nature of the relationship affects sexual intimacy.[92] We are whole people. Medical and psychological factors, sexual knowledge or lack of it, communication between partners, marital harmony, sexual anxiety and worries about performance all affect sex life – for example, preventing a woman from being able to enjoy orgasm.[93] In one programme, 135 couples were given individual counselling, sessions with each other, or with groups of others. The most popular were the couple sessions.[94] Couples' therapy may not work if one partner has a 'big agenda' of his or her own; in this case, it is often necessary to meet first with each partner separately.[95]

So, then, we have seen the terrible emotional price that many are paying today for relational chaos, fragmented experiences with different people, the trauma of breaking up after years, loneliness and childlessness in middle life, and a big rethink about the future. A big element of this has been made worse by the sexual revolution, with its emphasis on sexual freedom and its denial of the emotional consequences.

We have seen that it is very possible for people to enjoy long-term, happy, loving relationships that are deeply fulfilling. Research has helped us to understand how to make this more likely, and, where relationships are struggling, we are finding many practical ways to help.

The writing is there on the wall: the revolution in sexual relationships not only makes many ill or kills them with sex diseases like AIDS, but also wrecks people emotionally, often scarring them for life. What is more, it is all so unnecessary. But if that is what has happened to so many adults, what about the children?

6

THE BROKEN GENERATION

Every week, we are becoming more and more aware that the promotion of sexual freedom is wrecking children's lives as well as those of adults. We are recognising that love between parents, or the lack of it, can greatly affect child development and emotional health. Children don't just sail through parental conflict, separation, divorce and remarriage: there are lasting consequences. Children are affected by single parenting too, and step-parenting has often turned out to be no substitute for a missing father or mother.

The changes in parenting have been dramatic. In the United States a third of all babies are now born outside marriage, as in the United Kingdom.[1] In Australia, the figure is lower: one in five in 1986.[2] Half the children born in the United States between 1970 and 1984 are likely to spend time in a mother-only family, and half of these are expected to acquire a step-parent by the age of 16.[3] In Britain, there are 1.3 million single parents looking after 2.2 million children.[4] The proportion of single parents in Britain is three times the rate of Spain or Italy, and six times the rate of Greece.

Traditional parenting still seen as an ideal

In 1993, almost six out of ten people said they believed that children needed a home with both their mother and their father in order to grow up happily, and four out of ten said that they thought that a single mother could not bring up her child as well as a married couple.[5] Thus the two-parent family remains a strongly held ideal.[6] In other European nations such as Italy or Spain, with more traditional families, the two-parent ideal is even stronger. The same survey found that only 35 per cent were happy about unmarried people having children.

The director of the UK National Council for One-Parent Families has said: 'Clearly, people do still believe that two parents who are loving and supportive are the best for children, but they have recognised that where this is not feasible, women can manage quite well alone and can be extremely good parents.'[7] The reason there is such a drive to recognise the needs of single parents is because bringing up children on your own can be a real struggle and, without help, children can suffer.

Either we say that single parenting does not cause any problems, so single-parent families can be treated just the same as all others without risk to adults or children; or we say that single parents face many difficulties, and therefore the state needs to step in to help fill the gaps – mainly for the sake of the children involved. The truth probably lies somewhere between the two, and of course some single parents will need more support than others. On balance, though, single parenting can be very tough.

A bad marriage may be better than divorce

It was common in the past for couples to stay together 'for the sake of the children'. However, this attitude changed during the 1970s and 1980s to 'better a good divorce than a bad marriage'. Three out of four British adults in 1986 said one partner ceasing to love the other was a sufficient reason for divorce.[8] By 1993, only one in three British women said they would stay in an unhappy relationship for the children's sake.[9]

Possibly the change of attitude has come out of an emphasis on personal fulfilment; or perhaps it was because of the influence of psychiatrist philosophers like Dr R.D. Laing, who were very negative about the whole concept of family, or people such as psychologist David Cooper, who wrote *Death of the Family* some two decades ago. Perhaps the change of attitude was partly the result of the first figures from the National Child Development Study, which started in 1958: these suggested that pre-divorce quarrelling was the major source of damage to children, so it might be best for them if unhappy couples separated quickly. That finding is now being questioned after further analysis.[10]

There is now strong evidence that living in an unhappy marriage may be far better for children than separation or divorce. The Joseph Rowntree Foundation funded important research by Dr John Tripp and Monica Cockett at the University of Exeter.[11] Their preliminary findings were very disturbing, and made headlines in February 1994.[12] They looked at what happened to a carefully matched sample of 152 children aged nine to ten and thirteen to fourteen. Half of their families had broken up one or more times.

Divorce wrecks children emotionally

John Tripp and Monica Cockett found that children from broken families were twice as likely to have problems with emotional and physical health, behaviour and attainment at school. They were also more likely to suffer from low self-esteem and have difficulties in friendships.[13] They were four times as likely to suffer stress-related health problems such as headaches, bed-wetting, or stomach aches, 'feeling sick', not wanting to go to school, or just 'feeling miserable'.[14]

Those in step-families fared even worse, and were six

times as likely to have these problems. Children whose families broke up more than once did worst of all, and were eight times more likely to suffer from psychosomatic illness, to need help at school, or referral to an educational psychologist, and ten times as likely to be badly behaved.[15]

Children from divorced families were four times as likely to need to see a psychiatrist. Perhaps this is part of the reason why the number of teenagers and children admitted to British psychiatric hospitals with serious mental illness has increased by almost 25 per cent in the five years from 1986 to 1991.[16] Admissions among children under the age of ten doubled from 707 to 1,400. In those aged 10–14, the numbers rose from 1,077 to 1,600. Part of the rise has been blamed on the lack of proper community psychiatric support, but others believe that parents splitting up is also a major factor.[17]

Children may be happier for parents to quarrel than to part

The research showed that constant fighting between parents had less adverse effects than parental separation,[18] and the end result on children was closer to that in 'happy' families.[19] These are very serious findings that demand an urgent rethink about long-term commitment in relationships before people have children. Dr Tripp is very clear that neither poverty nor conflict had caused the damage – it was the loss of a parent: 'What parents don't realise is that while they may have problems with each other, the children often have good relationships with both parents – and they lose that when the family breaks up. In addition, the separation often did not end the conflict.'[20] In some cases the conflict itself was made worse by separation, because children were drawn into it for the first time. Three out of four non-custodial parents said, after putting their children through all this, that they now wished they had never divorced.[21]

We need to get this message through to every family where parents are in difficulties. Separation is likely to significantly damage your children; and, looking back, you may regret what you have done, and wish you had tried a little harder to work it out – especially when you realise the price your children have paid.

Although the Exeter study made big headlines in the United Kingdom, another lesser-known British study of 111 families in Edinburgh, by Dr Ann Mitchell, discovered similar things almost a decade earlier. She also found that children prefer parents to stay together, even if they argue and fight.[22] Her work was based on interviews of teenagers and their custodial parents five years after divorce.

Children have such a powerful sense of belonging, linked to their own search for love.[23] Children are also creatures of habit, as any child psychologist or parent knows, responding to routine, familiarity and disliking change. Although children were sometimes included in discussions about which parent they lived with, this decision was usually influenced by previous decisions about who was going to keep the family home. It was rare for children to be able to choose to go on living in the same place and with whoever they wanted.

Moving to relatives' homes almost always resulted in overcrowding. Sometimes the whole family would be crammed into one room, with shifts for cooking or eating meals. Some mothers had returned with the children to the family home to find everything gone: in one case, all the furniture; in another, the toys; or in yet another, all the plants in the garden.

One in four had moved home three or four times. One girl had moved at least six times with her mother and ten times with her father. She was very sad that she had never managed to stay long enough anywhere to make any friends. Obviously, her schooling had been severely disrupted.

Children have to grow up and 'make do'

The children often landed up with adult responsibilities, 'covering' for an absent parent: cooking, washing up, doing laundry, maintenance, babysitting, gardening, decorating, shopping. They grew up prematurely because they *had* to.

Poverty was common, and maintenance disputes strained many relationships. Some women were convinced that former husbands were deliberately not getting work to avoid maintenance, and one mother said that every time she went to see her solicitor, her ex-husband went back on the dole.

Very few talked to their children about what was going on in much detail. Children often turned to grandmothers and grandfathers for comfort, because they were well known, well loved – and also, *in* the situation, yet partly outside it. They were also more available. Parents often seemed to deny that their children had many feelings about the divorce. Eight parents mentioned truancy and other behaviour problems that they felt were due to the divorce, but blamed it all on the other parent. Others mentioned clinginess, being withdrawn, aggressive behaviour, and various other problems.

The children often felt very upset. Frequently, they hid their distress, crying alone in their rooms at night, sobbing at school, or when their parents were out. Many tried very hard to protect their parents from seeing their pain. Some children were furious with the parent they blamed for breaking up the home. Feelings of rejection were commonly felt by the children, usually by the same-sex parent.

Surprised and embarrassed, but rarely relieved

Some of these children were surprised by the separation; others were embarrassed that their friends knew that they lived with only one parent. Therefore the fact that their parents are divorced may be hidden by children from all but their closest friends.

The only children relieved by the divorce (7 out of 111) had fathers with severe alcohol addiction, or whose behaviour was bizarre in some way. One was relieved when his mother divorced a stepfather he disliked. Only five said that they were unhappy before their parents divorced, and only half remembered any parental conflict. The children had responded to conflict in various ways: telling their parents to stop arguing, running out of the house, hiding under the bedclothes and being unable to sleep, or bursting into tears in the same room – which was often the most effective behaviour.

Half the children had wanted reconciliation to take place, and some were still clinging to this hope five years later. None of the children blamed themselves – this is something that younger children may feel, but rarely teenagers. The worst result of separation was that they felt they did not see the parent they didn't live with often enough – if at all. The next worst thing was being shunted around from place to place, followed by a shortage of money.

Access was difficult, even when arrangements worked well – but they often failed to work well, with disagreements, or parents letting each other down. When they happened, access visits were often tedious or expensive, or both. Mothers often took children to the shops or a café. Fathers more often chose a film, football matches or swimming. Fathers more often had a car, so this helped.

The trouble is that there is no adequate substitute for

parents and children enjoying living together in the same home, wandering in and out of each other's company in an informal and relaxed way. Some children actually scorned the amounts lavished on them during visits by an estranged parent. Five years after divorce, only one in ten enjoyed a warm relationship with an absent parent, and only one in four living with their mothers had stayed overnight at their father's home. No child living with a father had ever slept in a mother's new home.

Parents were often very curious about their ex-partners, gently pumping their children for information after visits, which was very hard on the children. It was difficult for adults to draw the line between interest in what the children had been doing, and curiosity about the ex-partner's new life. One child said that the constant questioning had 'torn her apart'. Both parents were always asking about the other, so she stopped seeing her father. Some children made secret visits, slipping away after school to see Mum or Dad.

New relationships were often resented

New relationships were common, often leading to remarriage, although in 1 in 50 cases the parents patched up their differences and came together again. There tends to be less romantic love in remarriages, and more emphasis on practical and financial advantages. As with divorce, there was little discussion with the children concerning a new relationship. It was usually assumed that the children would just accept a new partner in their parent's bed. In practice, their feelings ranged from warm love to strong resentment. One in four never accepted the new partner.

Teenagers were more likely to resent new relationships than younger children. In almost every case, first names were used rather than 'Mum' or 'Dad'. Only 5 out of 111 came to see the new person as a parent – and in every case, it was where divorce had happened at a very young age, so there were few memories. Attitudes to a step-parent's own children were closely related to feelings about the step-parent, again ranging from affection to hostility.

In summary, the Edinburgh research shows us 'parents can change partners, but children cannot change their parents although they can gain extra ones'. Both the Edinburgh study and the Exeter study highlight the terrible price paid by the 'broken generation', coping with the sexual chaos of their parents.

More problems before and after divorce

Two large studies of groups of children born in 1946 and 1958 have also suggested that children fare badly after divorce, even as adults. These studies showed that they were more likely to leave home early, marry in their teens, have children before the age of 23, and were more prone to emotional or psychological problems – particularly in their mid-thirties, and especially if they were women.

The effects were lifelong: by the time they were in their forties, these child survivors of divorce were more likely to have lost contact with their parents, even the one who brought them up.[24] However, social conditions were different then in terms of stigma and isolation. So what about more recent work?

In January 1994, the UK Family Policy Studies Centre tried to draw together all the research on lone parents and family disruption.[25] The overall consensus is that children who are the products of divorce and single parenting do worse in almost every respect – for example, in read- ing, writing, maths, anxiety levels and bad behaviour.[26] Divorce and separation is the worst environment, followed by single parenting, which later becomes step-parenting or single parents who stay as

single parents. The children of widows seem to suffer least.

One study discovered that children born outside marriage were on average ten months behind on reading
age, after correcting for any bias caused by background,
intelligence or other factors.[27] These children did worse at
reading and maths, got poorer exam results than expected,
and got worse jobs later on.[28] One study in Cardiff in 1994
looked at young people who dropped out of education,
training, apprenticeships and jobs. Many came from broken homes.[29]

Across Britain in 1994, there were 76,000 young people
who had left school, yet had slipped through the training
and benefit 'safety net', a new generation of 'dead-end'
teenagers. Some were at home with parents, but with
no income; others were begging on the streets.[30] Every
generation feels scandalised by its youth. Socrates wrote
almost 2,400 years ago: 'The young of today love luxury.
They have bad manners, contempt for authority and
disrespect for their elders.' However, there do seem to
be very worrying underlying trends today, clearly linked
to the destruction of family life by the sexual revolution.

We cannot possibly go further forward in the same
direction when faced with the results. Adults may survive
relationship burn-out unscathed, but the evidence is clear
that their children will not.

Time to think again about two-income parenting

Given all of these things, it is hardly surprising that we are
seeing a change of heart by major opinion-formers about
the sexual revolution, and what is good for children. Take
Penelope Leach, for example, whose books on parenting
influenced a generation. As Angela Lambert writes in the
Independent:

She was THE child care guru for the seventies; the companion of every mother's sleepless nights, of every helpless parent in despair as a toddler screamed himself blue, of every out-of-practice granny giving young parents a weekend off. Her book *Baby and Child* has sold more than two million copies worldwide in twenty seven languages.[31]

In Penelope Leach's latest book, *Children First*, published in 1994, she is now promoting the view that children need parental attention, and that the values of society have undermined parenting as a 'worthless activity'.[32] In other words, society today often gives the impression that you are less of a person if you stay at home with your children.

She is now telling the millions she influenced, and the new generation that followed, to reorder their priorities and to devote more time, energy and money to children – especially during their earliest years. She says that young mothers should think about delaying a return to work, and says bosses need to be far more understanding:

I find it disgusting that women have to pretend to have a migraine in order to persuade an employer that they need to stay at home to nurse a child . . . Rearing new people is at least as professional and creative as any high-status job. We know that what happens to children is terribly important, both to them and to society's future . . . People must realise that phrases such as 'children are our future' do have meaning – if you once get men to see it. We *can* afford the resources for people who wish to give two or three years to each child out of a 40-year professional life. The fundamental problem is that people just don't think children are important.[33]

Mothers at home feel 'odd'

One married mother at home with the youngest of her four children said recently: 'I know I'm an oddity. People who choose to stay at home are ridiculed, aren't they? Mothering is regarded as a second class job. If I couldn't have looked after a baby myself I wouldn't have had one. But just because I'm at home it doesn't mean I don't know what's going on in the world . . . at least my children know they're my first priority.'[34]

Mary Anne Sieghart wrote in *The Times*: 'For many the "love that dare not speak its name" is that of a working parent for a child . . . Trapped in a working environment which prevented us from spending more time with our children: not just time we would *like* to spend with them, but time we fear they *need* from us. You see, having children is not a hobby . . . We compared our feelings of guilt . . .' She describes a conversation with another political journalist, also a working parent, who remarked: 'You know there are only two kinds of people in the world. Parents of young children and the rest.' Two different worlds. Two different perspectives. Two different sets of pressures and priorities.

A change in job structure and social attitudes will come, she feels, but 'the sadness for parents of my age, though, will be if the change comes too late for our children to reap the benefits. If theirs turns out to be the lost generation, will we ever forgive ourselves – or the attitudes that let us down?'[35]

Day nurseries are questioned as best

Penelope Leach points out that in the past, mothers and children were at home, but in extended caring groups of families and friends. Now virtually all productive work has been moved out of the home, so mothers have a starker choice. Either they go out to work with feelings that they may be neglecting the children, or they stay at home with the prospect of loneliness and boredom. Children in turn are separated from parents much more, so that natural apprenticeship into adulthood is lost. 'Instead of learning to do as adults do, they are learning to do as adults say.'[36]

In Australia, Penelope Leach's views have caused uproar, particularly for suggesting that day nurseries are quite inappropriate for children under the age of three, but in the United States the idea of a generation of babies reared in groups has been causing some unease for a decade. Penelope Leach argues that babies and toddlers do far better when cared for by a parent, relative or childminder looking after her own and other children in an extended family. In Australia, day care is the commonest pattern.[37]

Penelope Leach also points out how employers have made family life harder: having to be at work for 48 hours of 48 weeks of 48 years, instead of allowing for flexible working. Giving up full-time work can be the end of promotion. We waste one to three hours a day commuting, and have lunch with colleagues instead of with the family. New patterns of home working, using the latest technology, might help.[38] Claire Austin of the Institute of Management agrees: 'It is not enough to have a workplace nursery. Companies must realise that women often have other responsibilities at home, and this makes life difficult if there is a culture where meetings take place at 5.30 p.m. and go on late.'[39]

Changes in British law giving full-employment rights to part-time employees will help many wishing to combine parenting with earning.[40] At the same time, changes in the economy mean that most new jobs being created are part-time.[41] Countries vary greatly in the allowances they make for children. In Sweden, all parents are offered 18 months' leave at the time of the birth of a child on 90 per cent pay, paid out of employers' tax. After that, they can opt to work a six-hour day until the child is eight. Swedish parents at home with small children are considered normal, and not penalised in their careers. They do not lose out financially or socially, since many other adults are doing the same.[42]

Choices, standard of living and prices

These arc big and emotive issues, and perhaps nothing is more guilt-inducing in grown men or women than the suggestion that the decisions we make are damaging our children. However, being a parent has big financial implications anyway. For one parent to stay at home a means being able to survive on one income, and many say this is impossible. For others, though, they are simply not prepared to go without a car, or a second car, or holidays, in order for one parent to stay at home.

Many of the most important things in life cannot be bought: love, care, affection, health – sex even, especially in a stable relationship. Look at the lives of the richest people on earth – their rates of depression and suicide are very high. For those in middle-income brackets or above, it can be true that however much you have, you never have enough, and however little you have, you tend to get by. (I am obviously not talking here about those who are fighting for their very survival financially.)

Double-income parenting has also enlarged the labour force at a time of recession. We live in a curious society where parents who feel pulled to be at home with their children are working hard in offices all day to pay their mortgages, while others without parental responsibilities are sitting at home on the dole. I am not saying that mothers rather than fathers should stay at home. I am simply pointing out that there are obvious, well-recognised benefits to children of having a parent

at home, and perhaps some hidden disadvantages when
both parents work.

'Parenting deficit' in the United States

There are other problems when both parents are out at
work full time. Who looks after children when they are ill?
What about half-term? What about school holidays? What
about life after school each day? Having friends round to
play? Supervising homework? Hearing them read?

The *Independent* recently carried an editorial on parenthood in the United Kingdom and the United States:

> There has been a recent and marked reduction in
> the time parents have for their children. The Ameri-
> cans call it the 'parenting deficit' . . . The number
> of hours the average American parent spends with
> their children has nearly halved in the past twenty-five
> years. The same pattern can be observed in Britain:
> harassed couples trying to juggle full-time jobs and
> family life. Single parents face even greater difficulties
> . . . Children suffer as a result . . . television and videos
> cannot replace guidance and support . . . There are
> hopeful signs . . . More fathers take their children
> to school but the domestication of the British male
> is painfully slow. For this, feminism must take some
> of the blame. It has tended to denigrate domesticity,
> making it harder for men and women to gain self-esteem
> through parenting. Only now, after winning battles in
> the workplace, have women begun to assert the value
> of looking after children.[43]

As we have seen, Penelope Leach may be facing an
uphill battle. In the 'me' generation, the only thing that
matters is *my* life, *my* feelings, *my* work, *my* pleasure,

my future, *my* relationships and *my* sex life. Everything else takes second place. The result of this is an atomised society; every relational link becomes devalued, because it involves sacrificing 'me' for 'we', laying aside some aspects of personal freedom to go forward together. Young children can almost cease to exist in an atomised world, and so can elderly parents.

However, empty individualism is slowly becoming discredited. Politicians of all parties are discovering that whatever their policies and the direction they would like to lead us in, it is hard to lead a bunch of individualists, and to build out of such a separatist group a cohesive, stable, caring, ordered society.

Big US rethink on children

Amitai Etzioni, Professor of Sociology at George Washington University and President of the American Sociological Association, said recently in a pamphlet for the independent American think-tank Demos that children had been sacrificed on the golden pedestal of careers and of 'making it'. Two generations of 'celebrating greed' in two-career households, with child care relegated to others, had produced a generation of 'neglected children':[44]

Now we have seen the result of decades of neglect of children, the time has come for both parents to revalue children and for the community to support and recognise their efforts. Over the last twenty five years we have seen the future and it is not a wholesome one. With poor and ineffective community child care and with ever more harried parents, it will not suffice to tell their graduates to 'just say no' and expect them to resist all temptations, to forgo illegal drugs and alcohol and to postpone sexual activity.[45]

Millions of mothers over the last 20 years have reduced their hours in the 'parenting industry' by working outside the home, while many fewer (and often poorly paid) people have taken on child care. Half the parenting labour force has been lost, and replaced by fewer, less qualified, people – yet we still expect the same quality of product.[46]

Of feminism, Professor Etzioni has said: 'Few who advocated equal rights for women favoured a society in which sexual equality would mean that all adults would act like men, who in the past were relatively inattentive to children.'[47] He has called for a wide range of government measures.

Single parents have had a hard time

So much, then, for the disastrous effects of separation and divorce on children. What about single parenting? Surely one way to avoid the trauma of separation is not to bother with a long-term relationship in the first place?

We have all read and reacted to comments by politicians that seem highly bigoted regarding single-parent mothers. Many of us are fed up with insensitive verbal bashing of single parents who are desperately struggling, coping with all the traumas not only of failed relationships, isolation and loneliness, but also of crippling poverty and the pressures of having to provide as one parent what children normally find in two. I have often felt very doubtful about some of the things said – especially on the political extreme right – since I have seen no concrete evidence to back their statements up.

However, as I have researched this book, I have trawled through literally hundreds of recent research papers on family, children, marriage, divorce and cohabitation, and the outcomes of the different living arrangements. They make very sobering reading for all of us, wherever we stand politically. Research should not be a party political issue; it simply creates an understanding on which policies can be better based.

In addition to researching the relevant literature, I have conducted a broader search by using the latest computer technology to sift through summaries of same 1½ million research papers published in scientific journals between 1989 and 1994. What follows are the patterns. (I have also added some personal experience.)

Single parenting is depressing and risky

We have already seen that raising children on your own as a single parent can be very depressing if you are on a low income, and that the break-up of households creates poverty.[48]

Depression in single-parent mothers also makes physical violence towards children more likely, as well as verbal aggression.[49] Moderate depression carries the highest risk of injury for children; this may be because the most severely depressed tend to be withdrawn and apathetic. A national US survey of 6,000 households found that single parents were more likely to use 'abusive forms of violence' with their children than two-parent households. There was a link between poverty and child abuse in the case of single mothers, but not with fathers.[50]

The link between single parenting and child abuse is more easily understood from one US study of two-parent families, which found a direct link between the closeness of the relationship between partners and how affectionate and caring they are with their three-month-old babies – even when differences were allowed for in individual adjustment to the pregnancy and birth.[51] Mothers in close/confiding relationships were more warm and sensitive to their children, while fathers were also more positive in attitude and role.[52]

Children enjoy a share in their parents' love

The message is that parents who love each other tend to express that love to their children. There is an overflow of positive feelings from the partnership to the products of that partnership. Where parents are in conflict, the children may suffer not just from the tension, but from a degree of emotional or physical deprivation compared to that which they would have enjoyed if their parents had been happy together. The protective shield around children is shattered by partner conflict.

As we have seen, the answer is not separation, which can make things far worse for children. The best solution for children is reconciliation, working things through, communicating, learning to listen again – all things that may require professional support.

Perhaps the breakdown of family life is part of the explanation for the doubling of rates of murder of babies less than a year old that took place in the United States between 1985 and 1990,[53] or the quadrupled national homicide rate for children between one and four years old during the same period.[54]

School performance affected by parenting

Returning to single parents, there is direct evidence that on average their children do worse at school; the difference is seen at almost every age and increases with time. These studies have taken great care not to confuse differences in background or intelligence, bearing in mind that, as we have seen, better-educated people divorce less, and more often get married before having children.

Ask any teacher which children are likely to be in greatest difficulties at school. Most will say that they can often tell which children are under great stress at home. It comes out in the journals they write, the accounts of their weekends, the comments they make in class, their emotional vulnerability, their behaviour and concentration. Some disturbed behaviour is due to mental difficulties, but in many others it is linked to what is happening at home. When the home situation settles, behaviour settles. When home flares up, behaviour worsens.

How do you teach a six-year-old to read when she is eating rubbers and making herself sick, urinating on the floor, and stealing all the biscuits from other children's lunch boxes or running out of the classroom? Most child psychologists would agree that such a child is looking for attention – a search for recognition, value, care and affection.

It is easy to get angry with such 'unreasonable' behaviour, until you discover that the problems suddenly got worse the day the father walked out a few weeks ago, leaving the family destitute. Now mother and children are homeless, sharing one room in a bed and breakfast 'hotel' where everyone is chucked out on the streets at 8.30 a.m. and not allowed back till evening.

Only a child once

Book after book on child and adult psychology points to the enormous importance of early childhood experience. You can only be a child once. For a child shunted between different homes, schools, parents and grandparents, the opportunities of those years have gone for ever. This is especially true when it comes to learning. Lost ground is often never made up. Time and time again, Sheila and I have seen it with people we know. They are stuck in jobs they find tedious and boring because family trauma wrecked their school years and destroyed their futures.

Also, the normal process of growing up and leaving home in a planned way seems to be more difficult if you have been brought up in a 'non-traditional family'.[55] A survey of over 4,000 Scottish teenagers found that family breakdown was a significant factor in the timing of many leaving home. For example, 44 per cent of those with a step-parent at the age of 16 had left home three years later, compared with only 33 per cent with a single parent, and 27 per cent with both parents at home.[56] One in four of those who left home before the age of 18 as a result of domestic tension were soon homeless, and six out of ten of all homeless young people gave family problems as the reason for their situation.[57]

The Children's Society in the United Kingdom reckons that one in seven of all children have run away from home at least once by the time they are 16. The police deal with 100,000 cases a year, but a survey of 1,000 children suggests that only the minority are reported as having run away.[58] Of course, when a child runs away from home, it is almost certain that his or her schooling stops too.

Thousands of teenagers end up sleeping rough on the streets of London. This disturbing trend has been blamed by some politicians on parents, while specialist care agencies blame the government for depriving many teenagers of the benefits they need to survive. These young people are just some of 400,000 registered homeless in Britain – a dramatic increase from only 170,000 in 1983.[59] The real numbers may be even larger.

Many homeless young people have been sexually abused,[60] but may then be at further risk of abuse on the street, or of being recruited by pimps. Terrible situations at home can contribute to a downward spiral of high mobility, fragmented relationships, sexually transmitted disease, unwanted pregnancy and future problems in bringing up their own children.[61]

Ill at home alone

Illness is another nightmare for single parents. All children get ill, and with every child the risk grows that one or more may be ill on any given day. What happens to the others? Two need to be walked to school. The other is vomiting every half-hour – and much too sick to walk a mile there and back, too young to be left. In an atomised, fractured society, where few neighbours or friends are at home during the day, what do you do? Where do you get help?

And what happens when you are ill yourself? Who steps in then? Some say, 'I just can't afford to be ill'. As a doctor, I know such a life has no margin, no reserve, no contingency; and people do get ill, very ill, for long periods – and can take a long time to die too. We try to deny such nasty thoughts and carry on living.

That, though, is hardly a satisfactory model of child-rearing. It may work most of the time, but we are gambling with our own bodies, and our children pay the price when our health breaks down. I am not talking about flu, coughs, colds or a migraine. There is more to medicine than that: broken legs, gallstone operations, appendicitis or worse. And a child in hospital is no joke either, even where there are *two* parents who are both able to take time off work. If several children are at home, the result can be total disruption, especially if the child in hospital is very young, and needing constant comfort and reassurance when feeling very unwell and distressed.

So what does a single parent do? Move the whole of family life into the ward? The risk doubles with two children, trebles with three, and so on. So much of the media image of single-parent families is naïve, distorted and impossibly simple. The image is of a single mother pushing a buggy; but having one child is a very different thing from a mother or father coping on their own with three or four, particularly with the added complications of different second parents.

Social support helps single parents

Support by friends can make all the difference, not just covering in times of sickness, but sharing the load in other ways. Research shows that where there are behaviour problems at home, extra social support for the single parent can help settle a child, particularly when combined with formal child management training for the parent.[62] Incidentally, being an only child in a single-parent situation may be particularly likely to result in emotional disturbance.[63]

Single parents have less time for attention

There is another problem that all single parents face: attention stretch. Recently, I looked after our four children aged four to eleven while Sheila was at a weekend conference. I was at full stretch – attention stretch.

Elizabeth wanted to show me her homework. Paul wanted help with his violin. John wanted to be taken to a friend's. Caroline and Elizabeth needed to be taken somewhere else. Elizabeth and Caroline were arguing over whose turn it was to play with a favourite new toy. Paul had fallen over and needed a cuddle. John wanted help to find a computer game . . .

Each of them wanted time from me, not from each other or even from another adult. Getting attention is the feeling that you are important to your mum or dad. All of us can remember proudly building a Lego model or a sandcastle on the beach, then crushing disappointment when Mum or Dad did not seem to care, made a passing comment, or were too busy or lazy to congratulate us on our masterpieces. Such things to some extent are an inevitable part of normal childhood, but at such times it feels as though no other affirmation will do.

An emotional crisis is common later on in life if a person realises they never had any real encouragement from Mum or Dad. Perhaps they were too busy, perhaps they didn't care, perhaps they were getting divorced, perhaps they were already divorced so there was only one of them.

Sheila and I have lost count of the number of times people have shared their sadness with us over these things. With separation, the need for affirmation by both parents grows – it does not get less.

Pseudo-parents and step-parents

Then we come to the thorny issue of pseudo-parents or step-parents. Blood ties are as powerful as the great dramas of fiction suggest; children have a massive pull to their own genetic parents, as almost all parents have to their own children, although this may take some time after birth to develop fully. That is why adopted children so often search for their genetic parents.

The effect is profound and psychological, based on knowledge and identity. We all try to make sense of who we are, and of our past.

A friend of ours discovered at the age of almost fifty that her 'parents' were not her parents after all. For all that time, she had no idea whatever. Yet in the moment of that discovery she was launched into a crisis, a search for her real identity. Who was her mother? Was her father still alive? She was unable to rest for months until she eventually found her mother, and finally her father too, which involved a trip to another country.

This pull of biology is why step-parents are usually on to a loser before they start if they try to fill a parental role. As we have seen, they usually do better to try to be an adult friend, an 'uncle' or 'aunt' rather than a mother or father. Step-parents are often puzzled, upset and confused by this rejection, but it is almost universal. (This is different from adoption of an older child, who for various reasons has chosen deliberately to adopt new parents in just as much of a commitment as the new parents have made in adopting the child.)

So parents are of paramount importance. Deep down, we all know that this is true – but we often live as though we don't really believe it.

More than one way to raise children

Are there any alternatives to the nuclear family that really work? For much of human history, the most common pattern has been the extended family, with three generations living together: grandparents, parents and children, and possibly other relatives also. Such households provide a stable base for growing children, with grandparents helping parents, who may be working in the fields or involved in other ways of generating income.

In the United Kingdom, such three-generational living is more common in those from ethnic minority backgrounds, whether Asian, Afro-Caribbean or other groups. In many white families, even *these* generational ties are collapsing. But what will happen in the next 20 years? The social insurance policy of an older generation with more stable relationships will not be there if present trends continue.

Already we are seeing therapists in danger of assuming parental roles for single-parent families. With no partner to help and many social pressures, the counsellor may be the only supportive person left with whom parent and child can work through their conflicts, in a way that might not have been necessary if both parents were still supporting each other.[64]

The broken generation grows up

The British National Child Development Study (NCD) is an ongoing study of 17,000 children born in the week of 3–9 March 1958. It has contributed much to our understanding of adult relationships and the impact on children. As in other studies, those divorced were more likely to suffer further 'relationship breakdown'. Once again, higher education and home ownership was associated with lower divorce rates.

The differences in education are very striking for lone mothers. British government figures for 1988 and 1989 show that only 2 per cent had a degree or equivalent, and 45 per cent had no qualifications at all. In other households with dependent children, 13 per cent had a degree or equivalent, and only 18 per cent had no qualifications at all.[65]

Where are the fathers?

A recent review of all research on single parents published by the Institute of Economic Affairs concluded:

> We have not yet come across, or succeeded in being directed to, any serious statistical study that shows on the average babies who have lacked a sociological father fare better than babies who have had a sociological father. But nearly all the serious statistical studies we have examined show that . . . they do worse. The longer the same father has been part of the child's life, and the more effectively the father has taken part in the life of the family, the better the results for the child.[66]

Oxford social scientist Professor Halsey, distinguished socialist and researcher, commented:

What should be universally acknowledged is that children of parents who do not follow the traditional norm (i.e. taking active and personal responsibility for the social upbringing of the children they generate) are thereby disadvantaged in many major aspects of their chances of living a successful life. On the evidence available, such children tend to die earlier, to have more illness, to do less well at school, to exist at a lower level of nutrition, to suffer more unemployment, to be more prone to deviance and crime, and finally to repeat the cycle of unstable parenting from which they themselves have suffered.[67]

In 1979–80, Professor Kolvin at the Nuffield Psychology and Psychiatry Department of Newcastle University led a study of a random sample of 264 men and women aged 32–33, looking at their experience of fatherhood by the age of 15.[68] The group had already been studied at various stages of development since birth.

He looked at deprivation, measured by parental illness, poor physical and emotional care of the child (personal and domestic dirtiness, poor clothing), debt, unemployment, overcrowding and general incompetence in the mother, and finally marital instability. Where fathers had been absent for all the child's life, the child was more than three times as likely to be suffering from multiple deprivation. (This was demonstrated after taking great care to eliminate other factors.) The children weighed less in father-absent families; one in three in multi-deprived families had speech defects at five years of age, and were four times as likely to have been burned or scalded in accidents.

The multi-deprived children were four times as likely to have criminal records as young adults; 15 per cent had been convicted at least eleven times – compared to only 2 per cent of the non-deprived group. Professor Kolvin also found that the presence of a natural father in the home was one of several powerful protectors against delinquency in teenage girls.

Divorce breeds divorce

And what happens to the children's children? What happens to a generation that has lost the memory and experience of happy lifelong partnerships? The answer is that they are more likely to divorce as well. Divorce today breeds divorce tomorrow. Divorce tomorrow risks more divorce in the future. Relationship destruction spreads like an infection, like gangrene, for generations to come.

As an undergraduate at Cambridge, I was friends with a female medical student, who told me she would never get married 'because of how it has hurt my parents'. She was so cynical about marriage that the question of divorce never even arose. She was utterly convinced that lifelong commitments were emotional suicide.

My wife and I have spent many hours helping couples in trouble. However, we always find it harder if one or both partners have *never* experienced stable adult relationships that worked.

Anyone can commit adultery

Adultery is particularly traumatic to children and to spouses, because adultery almost always involves deception and betrayal. Adultery is not just a single act of deception either. It is usually gross deception over a period of time within the most intimate of relationships, the betrayal of a companion, lover and friend. Open adultery (so-called 'open marriage') is hardly a recipe for happiness either.

Adultery can also be infectious. Break-up can lead to break-up, as more separated people fan out through the community looking for new partners. Some of those new partners may already be married – and so the havoc spreads.

Community living

An alternative to extended families for children is the commune idea of the 1960s. However, a much larger and longer-lasting radical social experiment has been observed for several decades.

The kibbutz philosophy of Israel makes a fascinating study. Here, a large number of people have committed themselves over long periods to give up individual rights and responsibilities, in order to gain individual freedom and corporate duties. Property is held in common, men and women do the same jobs for the same pay, and – most importantly – child rearing becomes a dormitory-based communal activity. So what happens?

The first thing to emerge is that while the ideals may be clearly defined, the practice has gradually altered. Parents are now seeking greater autonomy, and sleeping arrangements for children are once again becoming family-based. Extended families with blood ties have been a far more successful and enduring pattern for child rearing, compared to community living, although the latter can work if there are clearly defined, commonly accepted standards.

to summarise, it seems that community living is no answer to the traumatic experiences of children trying to cope with their parents' sexual adventures and relationship problems. There must be a better way, and we need to find it quickly. The answer, of course, is mutual faithfulness in a relationship that works.

So much for the great freedom of the sexual revolution. What started out as liberty has become a prison, a chain, a curse, a terrible burden carried by children while their parents are too busy sorting out their own problems to notice the full extent of the damage.

7

SEXUAL ABUSE AND OTHER CRIME

I now want to look at crime of all kinds, and ways it might be linked to the sexual revolution. The most obvious area where this is likely to happen is over sexual abuse. There have been many attempts to predict those families where sexual abuse is most probable, most notably the 1988–1990 study of UK child abuse trends.[1]

Sexual abuse of children has been defined as 'the involvement of dependent, developmentally immature children and adolescents in sexual activities which they do not fully comprehend, to which they are unable to give informed consent, or which violates social taboos of family roles'.[2] Sexual abuse traumatises children in a way that may dominate the whole of their lives, affecting all their relationships, especially sexual ones. It can affect self-esteem, self-image, self-worth and future marriage, and make future sexual difficulties far more likely.

So is there a link between sexual abuse and fractured partnerships? I am not referring here to a marriage that breaks up because a mother discovers her husband has been abusing their daughter. What I am asking is whether children of divorce or relationship break-up are more at risk of sexual abuse. Some will argue that it is very unfair to say that relationship breakdown is to blame for child sex abuse, and that the abusers themselves are to blame. Without doubt, those who abuse children for their own sexual gratification are rightly regarded as social deviants, criminals against which there are severe sanctions in any civilised society.

Yet many child abusers were abused themselves; thus an act of sexual abuse can have a knock-on effect. I am not in any way justifying sexual abuse or making light of it just because an abuser may himself or herself have been a victim of abuse. I just want us to understand the factors that may increase the risk of this happening.

Making abuse more or less likely

If there are conditions that shape a person's mental state so that abusing others sexually becomes attractive, there are also situations where that mental state is more likely to turn from fantasy to activity.

The first is a general culture that says 'me' is important. As we have seen, we live in an age where 'self' is everything, and responsibilities to others mean less and less. The argument basically is this: 'The child did not scream; the child did not shout; the child took part without emotional threats or physical violence. It felt beautiful to me. The child continued to see me and took part in more – how can that be the equivalent of violent rape? All I have done is taken away innocence and replaced it with early knowledge.' At root, these are the arguments of 'self': my drives, my needs, my desires, my rights, my freedoms. As we have seen, the old sexual revolution is powered by an obsession with 'self', and therefore sexual abuse is linked to it. Why else have the sexual abuse statistics soared?

Some say the rise in rape and sexual abuse figures are mainly because people are less afraid today to report these things. This is the same kind of denial that tells us that crime generally is not really getting worse. If crime isn't getting worse, why is it that communities that never used to lock their doors are now locking doors and bolting windows – *and* alarming the whole house? Why is it that anyone who leaves a bicycle outside a shop for ten minutes and has it stolen is now looked upon as stupid, whereas someone padlocking a bike in the same place some 50 years ago would have been considered almost paranoid?

If crime is the same as it was, why have insurance premiums soared? In Britain, the number of claims for theft rose from 410,000 in 1989 to 877,000 in 1992 – more than doubling in just three years – although they have dropped slightly since.[3]

Just as rape is on the increase, every other kind of socially unacceptable sexual behaviour has risen too – child sexual abuse included.

Paedophilia more acceptable today

Perhaps another reason for the rise in child sexual abuse is a rejection of previously accepted boundaries or guidelines for acceptable sexual expression. Paedophilia is more respectable than it was. In fact, paedophilia magazines and clubs are a big growth industry, something that would have been unthinkable in such an open way half a century ago. The media increasingly shows the whole of life as a potential sexual experience – from buying a car, to choosing the right brand of coffee, to going on holiday, to saying hello to a child.

We have seen previously how fashion editors came in for a hammering with a new look that seemed to be lifted straight from the classroom. Models chosen for their pre-pubescent looks were paraded in short skirts, frocks and hats that looked like school uniform. The image was disturbing to many, and there were a number of complaints. One British magazine showed a whole series of lingerie photographs, modelled as though by a young teenager beginning to explore her own sexuality. These too were criticised, for many thought the images were about child pornography – not about selling lingerie. One reviewer at one of the shows said she felt she was being involved in child pornography by just taking part, by just being there.

So, then, while a taboo may still remain, images have given a positive message that it is acceptable to enjoy sexually arousing pictures of children or of adults looking like children. This is all part of the sexual revolution.

The taboo itself has also been weakened, though. We live in a culture where all matters sexual are aired and debated as never before. When it comes to sex, there are few moral codes these days that are widely agreed. The philosophy of agony columns could be summarised in four sentences:

1 Whatever you do on your own is fine.
2 Whatever you do with another person is fine, as long as it is agreeable to you both.
3 Don't do it with children.
 but
4 Children are sexual beings, and part of growing up is that they will want to try out their sexuality on you – don't reject them.

The image of the old, gruff, sexually repressed, Victorian father who was too inhibited and disturbed by his daughter's developing sex appeal to ever give her a kiss, hug or compliment may have been replaced by a new, affectionate, sexually liberated, late twentieth-century father who is too uninhibited and excited by his daughter's developing sexuality to prevent himself giving her a sensuous kiss or an arousing cuddle. Both extremes are of course ones that most people would reject. Instead, we need a new model of fatherhood that affirms and respects, is affectionate yet restrained, is warm yet protecting.

So, then, the obsession with 'me' that is connected with the old sexual revolution, the changing moral framework, promotion of images arousing to paedophiles, and the relaxation of some taboos may all be contributing to the increasing epidemic of child sexual abuse.

Sex abuse by non-fathers

Important factors in abuse are partnership breakdown, relational chaos and step-parenting. Sexually abused children are 10 times more likely to be from step-fathering families than the national average, and least likely to be living with both natural parents.[4]

Step-children are usually older, and they often have a non-parent or 'friend' relationship with step-parents. This is more usually stepfathers, since natural mothers are most likely to have custody. The natural feelings of physical detachment, based on social taboos, may be far greater between a father and his natural, younger children, than between a man and a very attractive pre-adolescent girl, or girl in her early to middle teenage years with whom he has a 'special friend status'.

There is a further complication worth thinking about. If the girl has been greatly traumatised by the previous divorce or separation and disturbed by the new arrangements, she may well be expressing intense needs for affirmation, identity, value and affection.

This can then become an explosive mix, with the stepfather sliding step by step into an abusing situation with a girl who is also making some very encouraging gestures. The situation is further complicated by the possible history of the girl's own mother. If she knows her own mother got pregnant at the age of 15 and had sex for the first time when she was 13, that may also help create a culture where her daughter is half-way to the point of sexual experimentation before she starts. Role modelling on parents can be very powerful process.

At-risk registers

I want to turn now to other kinds of child abuse – what about at-risk registers, or children taken into care because of well-substantiated fears of neglect, injury or death? Again, sadly, step-parenting features prominently. It is just too much to expect all non-biological parents to have the same feeling for a child as biological parents. (However, it needs to be remembered that many *natural* parents are also abusers, and many step-parents offer children better parenting than they ever had from their biological parents.) Nevertheless, on average, all arrangements other than living with both natural parents seem to carry extra risks of child abuse.[5]

When it comes to physical abuse of children, the surprising thing to me as a doctor is that it does not happen more often. Considering how basically selfish we all are, it is quite extraordinary how few children do get starved, abandoned or beaten up. When a child is born, the parental instincts to care for it are extremely strong. It is a primeval bond, no doubt deeply entrenched in our genes, for without it the human species would not have survived. In fact, the parenting instinct is found in almost every mammal in one form or another.

Many future parents look with distaste and obvious detachment at the babies of others; they show no interest whatever. Perhaps more often this 'allergic' reaction is seen in men. Yet when their own children are born it is as if they have all had brain transplants. All of a sudden they are besotted with their own babies, and now cannot understand why others are not as captivated and entranced as they are.

Emotional 'rewiring' at birth

This emotional 'rewiring' happens inside our brains, taking us over in a new all-consuming parental role. Of course, as 'higher' creatures, there is much more to us than instinct, and these 'natural' feelings, pre-programmed in us for survival of our species, are often subsumed or obliterated by other emotions, events and demands.

The mother who feels nothing for her baby but resentment – is it because of relational chaos that she feels so trapped, so unsupported? The father who is totally rejecting of the child and violent towards it – is it because he feels trapped by an unwanted pregnancy into a relationship he would rather walk away from?

There are many reasons why people do not feel a great surge of maternal or paternal feelings. However, most people do feel them, and very few feel the same strength of feeling towards other people's children (except in the unique situation of adoption, and to a lesser extent in fostering arrangements). When your partner is the biological mother or father and you have no genetic link at all – only that you have had sex with the child's mother or father, and perhaps live together – those protective feelings are unlikely to be there to the same extent as if the children are your own; thus the child *may* be vulnerable in such situations.

Averages are important things, as we have seen throughout the book. Someone might say: here is a man who is not the father, yet who is an infinitely better carer than the man who is. Within every generalisation, you will find a huge overlap between the averages between two extremes. However, generalisations can still demonstrate basic truths.

It needs to be stressed here that adoption is a special case. Surveys show that adopted children in general fare very well: they learn quickly at school, and in other ways perform favourably. However, there are unusual or unique factors here. As we have seen, there is a severe shortage of babies to be adopted; and this means that the criteria can be very strict indeed for selected couples.

So, then, children are paying the terrible price of abuse, whether sexual or physical, emotional or mental, and much of this can be directly linked in one way or another to the effects of the old sexual revolution.

They are the broken generation, the silent majority of affected people. How does this brokenness affect them later on? In particular, does this brokenness encourage deviant behaviour? I want to look now at a detailed examination of youth crime and the new patterns that are emerging, because the evidence of a link with the old sexual revolution is growing rapidly, and is highly disturbing.

New patterns of crime

First, let us look at the pattern of crime, and then at the evidence for a link between crime and family life.

It is a well-known fact that much crime is committed by male teenagers.[6] One in five of all crimes are committed by those under the age of 14, and 1 in 20 boys has a criminal record by that age; 45 per cent of all crime is committed by those aged 10–20, particularly burglary and car crime.[7] In the United Kingdom, a third of all adult males have a criminal record by the time they are 33. So what is going on?

A number of explanations have been given for the rise in youth vandalism, street violence, car theft, burglaries and other crimes. As we have seen, some try to make out that the rise in reported crime figures is an illusion, and that it is just that people today are reporting crime more.

In 1861, the rate of recorded crime was 500 per 100,000 people. By 1990, it was 8,600 – a seventeenfold rise – and most of the increase took place in just 30 years, from 1960 to 1990. The increase in crime from 1990 to 1991 of 733,000 cases was greater than the entire annual total at the turn of the century.[8] Some of the increase may be due to the increasing population, from 20 million in 1861 to 50 million in 1991, but something else happened as well.

In the United States, the rises have been horrifying to many, seen in the daily diet of headlines and television news stories. In 1993, crime was the main topic on the ABC, CBS and NBC nightly news programmes.[9] Their coverage of crime doubled in a year from 1992, and news of murders tripled. One in five of all stories covered by the *Washington Post* in a typical week in 1994 were crime-related.[10]

Crime 'greatest threat to United States'

Surveys show that the US public now regards crime as the gravest problem affecting the country. As in the United Kingdom, some have argued that the supposed rises are simply due to an increase in media reporting. However, the level of violent crime per 100,000 people fell slightly from 1973 (32.6) to 1993 (32.1).[11] Not much of a drop perhaps, but certainly not a dramatic rise. Yet the risks of being murdered increased 23 per cent between 1985 and 1990. It more than doubled in black males between 15 and 24, and increased in white males of the same ages by 40 per cent.[12]

Whether rising, static or falling, the numbers are still enormous: over 26,000 homicides in 1990, and 31,000 suicides. From 1985 to 1990 the number of murdered babies under a year old doubled, and the homicide rate for children between the ages of one and four has increased fourfold in the past 40 years.[13] Coincidentally, this has almost exactly coincided with the period of the sexual revolution, and the breakdown of stable family life.

In the past 20 years, more than 50,000 juveniles were shot by other juveniles.[14] The former head of the US Child Protection Agency appeared on the television news and said: 'When children produce children and then try to bring them up in single families, in essence there will be a greater likelihood of them shooting other children.'[15]

In the United Kingdom, we tend to think that cities like New York have so much crime that it must be unbearable to live in them. Yet Manchester has a far worse crime rate for burglaries and car thefts than New York. With a mere 440,000 population, there were 64,000 burglaries and 58,000 stolen cars in 1991; in comparison, New York, with its 7.3 million population (around 16 times as large), only had 100,000 burglaries and 125,000 stolen cars.[16]

Different theories on crime

Depending on our world-view, we tend to interpret social problems as being caused by different things. For example, poverty, unemployment and social deprivation are often cited as major factors in the spiralling crime rates on some estates.

Janet Daley expressed the views of many in *The Times*:

Who is to blame for juvenile crime? Not us, say the courts and the judges: we have no powers to deal with under-age thugs. Not us, say the teachers: these children turn up at the school gates already out of control – when they turn up at all. And besides, the parents don't support our efforts. If we criticise a child's behaviour, his parents are likely to take the child's side. Not us, say the parents. 'I can't deal with him' wails the hapless mother whose 3ft 6in demon has just committed his 100th burglary, or absconded from his latest 'secure accommodation'. It's all the television he watches, or the estates we live on, or the rotten school he goes to, or the bigger children in the neighbourhood . . .

So the courts do not punish, and police do not apprehend, and the schools cannot threaten and the parents do not restrain, and they all deny they are responsible. Stepping into this vacuum, politicians have rather guilelessly allowed themselves to become a target for all the frustrated rage which everyone feels . . . It is a brave politician indeed who dares to say that the government is largely impotent in the matter of making people better.[17]

Let us look at the possibilities in more detail. Here are some suggestions that have been made:

> *Some explanations for big rise in crime*
> 1 Poverty and poor housing
> 2 Unemployment
> 3 Lack of community feeling/bad estate design
> 4 Lack of parental control
> 5 Divorce or conflict at home – a direct effect

Separating out the different factors

Can we separate out these different explanations? Many seem closely related. For example, there is an estate near our home where four out of ten are unemployed. Local community workers refer to it as the 'sink' estate, where 'problem' families tend to land up. It's the one area no one ever asks to be transferred to, and is almost entirely council-owned property. Hundreds are housed in high-rise blocks, while the low-rise housing is a rabbit warren of walkways, passageways, short cuts and other ways of disappearing to avoid arrest. There is no community centre. There are many single-parent families, and many elderly people living on their own are too afraid to go out.

So in such a complex situation, which factors on the above list are most important, or can they all have some effect? David Farrington, Professor of Psychological Criminology at Cambridge University, looked at persistent youth offenders and found as a group they had six things in common: low-income family, parent with a criminal record by the time the youngster was ten, harsh and erratic discipline at home, behaviour problems at school by the age of eight, willing to be daring by the time they were eight, low intelligence, and poor educational attainment.[18]

He discovered that persistent offenders were often sexually adventurous, but 'they rarely used contraceptives. They often had to get married because they had fathered a child.' They often got divorced, and many had already been married three times, with several other living-together relationships by the age of 32. The majority were using drugs before they were 18.[19]

Perhaps we need to conclude that there are many reasons why people turn to crime, and many factors that may make that more likely. However, almost all of these factors can be made worse by the sexual revolution, linking sexual chaos with youth crime. Let us consider a number of these factors or explanations in turn.

1 Poverty and poor housing

Many are convinced that there is a link between poverty and crime. The Association of British Insurers can predict some crime trends from trends in unemployment figures. For example, burglary peaked at the height of the 1989–93 recession, and has fallen since then.[20] But as Rosie Waterhouse wrote in the *Independent on Sunday* recently: 'If poverty in childhood is indeed the root of later criminality, it must be conceded that lone parenthood is the quickest route to poverty.'[21] Separation and divorce often mean selling a home or a move down the scale of home size.

Even the very wealthiest find that separation or divorce affects their standard of living. So when you are at the bottom of the earnings league before you start, where do you land up? The answer, for many people, is that they have to struggle by on state benefits. That struggle may continue through to old age. In fact, a new generation of elderly-poor is likely to emerge because of the rising divorce rate. Divorce reduces the amount families can save, and can cause long-term investments to be cashed in.[22]

For a family to split into two households means that the economic benefits of larger-scale living are lost: two homes, two cars, two packets of cornflakes. As any careful shopper knows, retailers heavily penalise those who cannot afford to buy in bulk. Poverty means you just survive from meal to meal, from day to day. You cannot afford to stock up for a month.

Poverty also means living in run-down areas where food prices are higher. In 1994, a survey by Barnardo's Charity of the Allerton estate outside Bradford was compared with Kensington in London. Seven out of ten on the Allerton estate are on benefits, and one in three is out of work, yet the cost of living is higher than in up-market London.[23] On some large estates, the only shops left are small ones, struggling to survive with lower turnover, higher costs, and constant security problems from vandalism, arson and theft. Larger supermarkets are some distance away, and beyond the reach of those without cars. Price differences are striking. In one run-down area of Cardiff, mothers were paying £1.74 more for a pack of disposable nappies than in Kensington.[24]

We know poverty is linked to many things. For example, a study in the *British Medical Journal* found that people on lower incomes die younger, and their babies and children are at greater risk of serious illness and death. Life expectancy for some of the poorest in Britain has *fallen* to 1940s levels.[25]

Poverty and deprivation have also been linked to drug

addiction, and addiction to crime to pay for the habit. Glasgow has more drug addicts per head of population than any other European city. Over 10,000 young people use £132 million of drugs every year. A House of Commons Scottish Affairs Committee concluded recently 'there is a clear correlation if not a causal relation' between drug addiction and poverty or deprivation. 'In areas where people are poor and families disintegrate more regularly . . . using drugs as a way of having a good time is more likely to be on the menu.'[26]

Iowa State University carried out a study of 622 teenagers from ninth to twelfth grades, and found that financial problems at home were linked directly to adolescent emotional difficulties, delinquency and drug use.[27]

So, then, the revolution in sexual relationships creates poverty, and poverty seems linked to crime.

2 Unemployment

Some say unemployment can lead to crime by damaging morale – not just because of a lack of income, but because it causes alienation, depression and despair among the young; these things can lead to vandalism, mindless violence and petty crime.

All this can be linked to separation and divorce in that emotional distress in children often damages academic performance, with some dropping out of school altogether. Early school leavers are the very group most likely to suffer unemployment.

Thus divorce, separation, complex new living arrangements, single parenting and other effects of the sexual revolution are all likely to result in increased numbers of unemployed teenagers and unemployable adults.

If we think that hopelessness about the job situation helps encourage a rise of teenage crime, then we have found another possible link between crime and the sexual revolution.

3 Lack of community feeling/bad estate design

Some say the soaring teenage crime rate is made worse by bad estate design and lack of community feeling. Bad design certainly makes it easier to commit offences and get away with it. We know that a lack of a feeling of community in many areas is also linked to crime. People tend not to steal from their friends, or neighbours they know, respect and trust. You are more likely to be recognised and traced in a small tight-knit local community.

The more people move around from place to place the fewer roots they have and the more anonymous life becomes – and divorce and separation usually increase mobility: children after separation have two parents, two loyalties, two sets of relationships, two addresses to give to a social worker or police officer if need be; and, as we have seen, they are more likely to change address several times.

If the parent with custody enters into a new relationship and the accommodation the new partner has is better, then the new relationship may involve yet another move.

All these factors tend to compound one another: children shunted around because of the sexual revolution are more likely to feel a stranger where they live, encouraging alienation. They are also more likely to feel insecure, vulnerable to peer pressure, searching for love and affection, vulnerable to sexual predators, missing out on schooling, unemployed or unemployable in a situation where money is extremely tight. The conditions are set for delinquency.

4 Lack of parental control

Some say the main reason for escalating teenage crime is not poverty or alienation, but lack of parental control. The sexual revolution makes parental control more difficult.

Bringing up teenagers is hard work, the struggle for their own identity is emotionally wearing to live with.

The natural challenge of authority as part of establishing independence, the contrariness and lack of consistency, can be both vexing and confusing.

Teenagers need time. Yet time is the one thing that separating parents may find it hardest to provide – and after separation, it can be even more difficult: one parent struggling to go out to work, also to do the shopping, cleaning, ironing, laundry, gardening, changing light bulbs, mending fires, arranging for the television to be seen to, paying the bills, doing the accounts, mending clothes, sewing on Brownie badges.

So if you take the view that the rise in teenage crime and delinquency is related to parenting, it is obvious that the sexual revolution is making parenting more difficult. There is a simple oversight function: two parents can more easily keep an eye on what their children are up to than one.

Finding a new partner is unlikely to help in the short term, because the process of building a new relationship is itself very time-consuming. It is very hard for single mothers to develop new sexual relationships, because former spouses, children and children of current partners can make life complicated, together with guilt over neglecting children for the sake of the new partner.[28]

5 Divorce or conflict at home – a direct effect
While we have seen a number of reasons why there could be a strong link in theory between the sexual revolution and crime, is there really any evidence in practice?

A large group of babies in New Zealand were studied over ten years of childhood, and then their risks of offending by the age of 13 were analysed. It was found in 1992 that exposure to parental discord during middle and early childhood led to increased risks of offending later. Major changes at home of various kinds did not have the same effect. There was a direct link, though, between delinquency and parental strife.[29]

Another 1992 study of 65 families with teenage sons in Texas looked at difficult child behaviour and parental relationship as perceived by the child. There was a strong link between parents who said they had great difficulties with their sons (out of control), and sons who said there was a lot of parental conflict at home.[30]

Many reasons why break-up may add to crime rate

So, then, we have looked at the unavoidable and disturbing fact that crime is increasing and that much of it is carried out by teenagers, and we have examined a whole range of possible factors that may be encouraging such a trend.

Whatever explanations we prefer may depend on our own personal experience, politics or perspectives on life, but we have seen that the sexual revolution may have had an added effect.

We will be looking in Chapter 10 at what governments can or should do, but in Chapter 8 we will look at the total economic costs to society from the sexual revolution. Even if some people still want and like the old sexual revolution, can we as a society afford it?

8

THE COST TO SOCIETY

What are the true economic costs of the sexual revolution? The greatest costs are those that are hardest to measure. If I am dying of AIDS, what is my life worth to me? I can only live once. My whole existence is being destroyed. What sum can possibly be adequate compensation?

While financial measures are a poor reflection of human suffering, it is still important to calculate the cost of the sexual revolution in cash terms. We will start with Britain, and then compare it with the United States and Australia.

Such costs are hard to quantify, except in general terms, so all figures have been rounded (usually downwards, since we are looking to find the *minimum* costs).

Health costs

The obvious place to start is health, and a significant element of this is AIDS. The AIDS cost is fairly easy to measure in Britain because the government has had a special AIDS budget. If we use a figure for care and prevention of around £210 million, we will not be too far wrong. To this we can add an estimate of productive years of life lost. Let us say that if 1,500 die of AIDS in the United Kingdom this year, the average number of working years lost per death will be around thirty (assuming an average age at death of 35). The total number of productive years of life lost because of AIDS will then be at least 45,000 a year.

Loss of productive life

Average earnings are £16,000 a year, and Actuary tables for loss of earnings of someone dying aged 35, assuming inflation and retirement at 65, are £360,000 per death.[1] This is almost certainly a gross underestimate for two reasons. First, many with AIDS in the United Kingdom are well educated, with higher than average earning power. Secondly, because the age of death is so young, the vast majority would have otherwise expected their earnings to increase with seniority over the next 30 years.

We can see that the loss of future income/earnings for those who die of AIDS in a given year could exceed £500 million over the next 30 years. You may say that in a nation of high unemployment, the economic loss of – say – an engineer is in fact an economic gain, because one less engineer will be drawing unemployment benefit or other means of social support. Although that is true in the short term, in the longer term the loss of skills, loss of labour force, and loss of consumers is far more significant.

More to sexual disease than AIDS

To the cost of AIDS, we need to add other sexual diseases. Let us say that it costs roughly £30 for each consultation in a sexual diseases' clinic, including diagnostic tests required during almost every consultation, and treatment costs. This will cover doctor and nurse time, administration and management, heat and light as well as maintenance, and a contribution to capital. There are around 580,000 such consultations a year. The total cost of out-patient treatment could be over £17 million a year.

Hospital care

What about in-patient care? This is unusual – advanced

syphilis, for example, is now very rare. However, if we include pelvic inflammatory disease (PID), we find large numbers of patients receiving treatment as in-patients.

The Royal College of Gynaecologists has around 1,300 members; however, some are retired. Let us say that at least 900 are in practice. One gynaecologist estimates that each one will have an average of 15 beds.[2] Of the 13,500 women in hospital at any one time, around 1 in 20 will be there because of PID;[3] that is, 675 women at a cost of £1,300 each week – perhaps £45 million a year.

Cervical cancer – prevention

Then there is the cost of cervical cancer – including the national screening programmes. Screening aims to check all women of reproductive age at regular intervals. Let us say that the costs of screening the average woman once, including doctor or nurse time, recall time, and follow-up is £15 per test, and a further £15 for laboratory costs. Around half the UK population of 58 million are female, and roughly 18 million are women between the ages of 20 and 64. The government's goal is to test each one every five years.[4] That gives us a bill for screening of around £100 million a year. In practice, not all are screened, but this would be the cost of screening if all women in this age group were tested.

Cervical cancer – treatment

Then there is the cost of treating cervical cancer, and the deaths and years of productive life lost. The UK death toll from cervical cancer per year is around 1,500. Ignoring completely the costs of treating nine others who are cured for each woman who dies, what are the direct care costs of those who die?

Let us assume a total of six weeks per person of in-patient care, from diagnosis to death, including biopsies, surgery, chemotherapy, radiotherapy and terminal care.

The cost per person will then be at least £7,000, to which we should add an element for out-patient care, family doctor time, community care at home, prescriptions of medication at home, and other things. The cost of all that could be £2,000 for each woman – probably more, particularly if someone is ill for a long period at home.

The total cost per case then works out at around £9,000 – far less than, say, someone with AIDS, for which the total bill for care can be as high as £25,000 to £40,000, partly because of the very expensive drugs needed to help fight HIV and other infections. A total care cost of £9,000 multiplied by 1,500 deaths a year gives us a figure of £13 million.

Pelvic inflammatory disease and infertility

Let us turn now to the other costs of chronic pelvic inflammatory disease – not the costs of in-patient treatment or medication, but the rapidly growing costs of infertility treatments. Let us take a rough figure of a half of all infertility treatments in women being needed because of sexually transmitted infections. In fact, the true figure is higher than this.[5]

Then let us use a rough figure of 5,000 per year for the total number of people receiving some form of assistance using in-vitro fertilisation (IVF), including all the counselling and tests leading up to it. The cost of a completed cycle of treatment varies, but can be as high as £2,500 in a London clinic.[6] Women have an average of three courses of treatment. Let us say the average treatment cost per cycle is £2,000.

Serono Laboratories, the market leader in infertility drugs, says that 40,000 cycles of treatment are carried out per year, which would give us a total IVF cost of around £80 million – which should be the total IVF costs of the 200 IVF centres and associated research laboratories throughout the United Kingdom. The size of this industry is increasing at 20 per cent every year. If we say at least half of these treatments are needed as a direct result of previous sex disease damage, that will give us a minimum of £40 million as another cost of the sexual revolution.

Other health costs

There are a number of other health costs to be considered. I am not including here increases in community care costs, many of which are social services costs rather than health. We will consider those later.

One family doctor with ten years' experience of general practice in South London reckons that 20 per cent of his work during that time was taken up 'directly or indirectly with the short, medium or longer term effects of extra-marital sex'.[7] He was including among other things his work in the area of AIDS, cervical cancer, infertility, and other problems we have already costed in specialist time only.

He was also including advice to teenagers on contraception and pregnancy, and also advice for those seeking terminations, including pre-and post-termination support. He also reckoned that a significant element of the huge amount of time spent on people with psychosomatic complaints was related to stress or guilt following affairs or other extra-marital relationships.

There are around 30,000 family doctors in the country, with an income plus add-ons of around £45,000 a year, not including all the practice costs of around £35,000 for ancillary staff, buildings and medication. Just a fifth of that salary bill would be £600 million. Even if we say the estimate is high, and settle for just a quarter of it, or 5 per cent of total workload, that will still add £150 million of family doctor salary costs caused by the sexual revolution.

We ought also to add an element for terminations. There were 182,000 abortions in Britain in 1992, of which

142,000 were in single women.[8] The cost of an abortion in a non-NHS clinic is around £200. Let us take an average figure of £150, since many take place in the NHS and the costs are slightly lower. That will give us an abortion bill of around £20 million a year. While some of this is due to contraceptive failure, some of it is the result of not using contraceptives in a short-term relationship.

Unplanned conceptions in marriage are far more likely to result in a birth, which is why the abortion rate in married people is far less. Many who have abortions are young; one in four of the 142,000 abortions in single people was for women below the age of 20.[9]

The additional health costs then add up to £170 million.

The health costs so far stack up as follows:

Some health costs of the sexual revolution (per year) (minimum)

	£ (millions)	
AIDS care and prevention	210	
Years of productive life lost	500	
Sub-total		710
Other sexual diseases – clinics	17	
in-patient	45	
Sub-total		62
*Cervical cancer – screening	100	
care – in-patient/community	13	
Sub-total		113
*Infertility-IVF	40	
Other health costs	170	
Sub-total		210
TOTAL		£1,095

* Proportion attributable to sexually transmitted disease or related factors. Much of this is private treatment.

There are other health costs too, which we will see

later – for example, the effect of divorce on family doctor consultations and the increased costs of community care. The health costs of the sexual revolution are therefore considerable, even in a nation like the United Kingdom with a low incidence of HIV. The total costs are probably over £1 billion a year, or almost 3 per cent of all health spending. If this money were diverted elsewhere, it would pay for some 1,500 primary schools annually.[10]

We're talking about a lot of money. Sex is not only unhealthy in many situations, but treating the sickness is very expensive indeed.

Divorce costs

Let us turn from health to the economic effects of household disruption; divorce cost calculations, though, are bound to be a very incomplete catalogue of the sheer scale of relationship breakdown, because, as we have seen, so many relationships are not formalised by marriage in the first place. Therefore any calculations based on marriage figures and divorce will underestimate the true total cost. However, it is also true that where marriage has taken place, there are extra legal costs involved undoing the agreement.

Let us first look at the cost of divorce alone, and then we can look at what we need to add on for non-marriage partnerships that break up, or for single adults who have children.

Legal bills

First, there are legal costs of divorce: solicitors, barristers and court time. Some proceedings go on and on, especially if custody over children is contested or both parties keep returning to court over access disputes, threatening behaviour or other issues related to property.

The average legal bill for a divorce is £1,650.[11] In

practice, most divorce disputes are settled by agreement between solicitors and barristers who negotiate out of court.[12] Most costs are legal-aided, because so many getting divorced are already on very low incomes, and wealthier people try to avoid court costs.[13] Some £180 million of the £1 billion spent on legal aid each year is on divorce.[14]

However, mediation as an alternative costs only £557 on average, according to a pilot scheme carried out by National Family Conciliation. Eight out of ten couples reach agreement on at least some issues, and four out of ten reach a complete settlement.[15] Legal aid work is poorly paid on a fixed cost per case: junior staff do most of it, with up to 200 cases each. Therefore there are often long delays.[16] One partner may also stall things to delay or get agreement to reduced payments.[17] Mediation can help speed things up in a situation where both partners have agreed on divorce, but are just trying to agree terms. This is different from mediation aimed at reconciliation and restoring the relationship.

Second homes are dear

What about rehousing costs? Most separations result in new households, at least until new relationships form, when two households may be rolled into one and the process reversed.

However, even if this reversal occurs, there are some unavoidable costs. Moving is expensive, even for one partner going into a rented flat not too far away. The flat may not be fully furnished, and even if it is, it is unlikely to feel like a real home as it is. People usually want their own furniture, cooker, television, curtains and other things – but they all cost money.

Moving, relocation and other costs are likely to be at least £1,000, but by the time a complete new household is set up the bill could be twice that. If the house or flat is privately rented, there may be an arrangement fee – which could be the equivalent to two weeks' rent. Telephone installation will probably be needed – and so the list goes on.

Finally, there are all the ongoing costs of running a second property. If a couple wished to rent or buy an extra holiday home, to have it available all the year round, providing heat in the winter, what would they need to put aside? The answer is a small fortune, which is why so few people own or rent second homes – yet that is precisely what happens at separation, unless a partner goes to live with parents or friends.

So let us quantify these costs.

First, there is rent. Even if the people are on income support, or are in council properties paying little or no rent, someone is paying the cost somewhere. The land was bought, capital is tied up, homes were built and need to be maintained. Therefore it is reasonable to take a commercial rent as a real measure of cost, since it is stacked in such a way as to cover both true running costs and capital servicing.

However, we need to add other costs such as electricity, gas and water, telephone rental, extra television licence, extra items to maintain and replace. Food is, as we have seen, far more expensive for smaller households, so food bills across both will increase.

So, then, how do we estimate the average total annual cost of this new home, extra food costs and other expenses? It seems to me that it would not be unreasonable to put a minimum figure of £250 per month or £3,000 a year – a figure depending greatly on the area and property type.

Counselling support and illness

Then there are the costs of counselling and advice to partners – and children too – over the entire period, bearing in mind that the roots of divorce often come some years before. Much of this is likely to be provided by family doctors and their staff.

Health can break down, and a cold or flu is more likely to knock someone flat when they are emotionally exhausted. The family doctor may be presented with a myriad of complaints from partners or children – ranging from insomnia, to anxiety, stress, ulcers, skin complaints, migraines, or bed-wetting in children, asthma, etc.

A significant proportion of the total workload of a family doctor can be supporting families where divorce is looming or has happened. I am told by those in general practice that a divorcing couple are likely to generate at least eight extra consultations of one kind or another for various family members, over a year or two around the time of separation. This would give a cost of over £300 at a calculation of £40 per consultation or home visit. I have included this figure in the health costs we saw earlier, but other counselling costs could come to £150 per divorce on average.

Benefit costs

Because many of the second households are poor, a large element of the above costs is borne by the state. This is to cover some direct costs of divorce, such as enabling a single-parent family to survive. There are additional benefits that single parents receive, for which two-parent families do not qualify. For those already receiving benefits, there is a lone-parent premium paid per week.

Therefore there is immediately a £260 annual present from the government, tax-free, for any couple on benefits who decide to separate, and this is repeated every year. Couples have been known to officially separate, but continue to cohabit, running two council homes in order to get more money. The second home can then be sub-let to friends.

In 1993, the total cost of income support and family credit for 1.3 million single-parent families was £3.4 billion, expected to rise to almost £5 billion by the year 2000.[18] One reason this is so high is that Britain has one of the lowest rates of single mothers in work, compared to other European countries.[19] Increasing family credit to help pay for child care would help, but would cost £100–200 million.[20]

Job costs

Then there are health costs that employers pay, because of lower productivity. Absenteeism is common at times of high stress. Let us say that the total time off for all reasons including moving out, court hearings, solicitors' briefings and illness is no more than a week.

In addition, there is a loss of concentration. Let us say output is 40 per cent reduced for an average of a month – or 20 per cent reduced for eight weeks. Many employers might put it a lot higher – and in my own experience of work colleagues, so would I. It is often a devastating time, especially if adultery is involved.

So let us put the total cost of time lost per divorce at around £1,000, for both partners. In many situations, two jobs are affected.

It all mounts up

It becomes abundantly obvious that this is all getting very expensive – it may be affordable for the wealthy, but it is bankrupting for others. In fact, it is so expensive to separate that some have suggested that economic factors are still a tie holding many relationships together.

So how does the total cost of a divorce begin to stack up?

Cost of an average divorce

	£
Legal costs[21]	1,650
Moving/relocation/setting up second home	2,000
Counselling/advice	
Extra doctor attendance	150
Absenteeism/lowered output	1,000
Additional household cost per year	3,000
TOTAL	£7,800

Some of these costs arise only once, while others may continue for many years.

Five-year costs could be £20,000

The first-year cost of divorce could be around £8,000, dropping thereafter to £3,000 per year. The cost in the first five years alone would therefore be around £20,000 per divorce, assuming that partners remain single and live on their own for five years after separation.

Obviously a new relationship brings cost savings from combining households. Although some do find new relationships very quickly, others stay single for many years. If the average time for both partners to find new partners is five years, then the figure of £20,000 remains correct.

There were more than 170,000 divorces in 1991,[22] so the total cost to the community of marital breakdown is probably around £3.4 billion. Therefore we can conclude that divorce is an extremely expensive business, mainly because economies of scale are lost.

Living together, but separating, also costs money

So, then, the sexual revolution costs Britain £1 billion a year in health costs and years of productive life lost, and a further £3.4 billion in divorce/separation costs. Surely that must be it? Unfortunately, no. Thus far we have totally ignored the costs of the rapidly growing number of long-term cohabitees who are also breaking up.

Let us say that for every £10 of divorce costs, there are at least £5 of costs from non-marriage break-ups of long-term relationships. If this is correct, we should add a further £1.7 billion to our figures, making a total so far of £5 billion new relationship breakdown costs each year, plus the health costs of £1 billion, making a total of £6 billion.

More than sexual illnesses and separation

However, the costs do not stop there. There are broader society impacts of families breaking up, and support is expensive: social workers, health visitors, family therapists, child psychiatrists, special-needs teachers and extra community care costs. (The latter is needed because so many who are ill at home are those living on their own.)

Social worker time

Let us look first at social work support for families breaking up. As a doctor, time and time again the people I have been involved in supporting have also needed help, support and professional advice from social workers. While social workers cover a very wide spectrum, they have many roles to play at the time of relationship breakdown or divorce.

Here are a few of these roles: advice on accessing other advice and help; assessment of the family situation; child protection; at-risk supervision; representation in court; housing and benefit advice; counselling of estranged partners; informal marriage guidance; post-divorce 'bereavement' support; advice and help in furnishing a new home; specialist support for disturbed children; informal family therapy. I could list many more.

Roles may vary according to training, area and availability, but social worker time costs money. There are 9,000 members of the British Association of Social Workers, and a great many more social workers who are not members. Let us say that 10 per cent of members' time is spent supporting those experiencing marital distress or cohabitation breakdown. What is the cost of a social worker? This depends on many factors. Add together salary, national insurance, pension, travel, telephone, office, secretarial services, heat, light, office rent, stationery and management, together with caseload supervision. You will reach a figure far in excess of £24,000 a year – and it is probably nearer £30,000, depending on age, experience and degree of administrative support. Let us take the lower figure, though; this will be multiplied by the 900 social workers, and comes to some £22 million.

Children in care

Part of a social worker's role is supporting children in care: 66,000 in 1992.[23] Six out of ten children are fostered at an average cost of £102 per week; this is £5,304 per year, with a total bill of £200 million. The remainder of youngsters are in children's homes,[24] costing between £536 and £943 depending on the type of unit. If we take a rough cost of £30,000 each for 26,400 children, the bill is £792 million – giving a total 'in-care' cost of around £1 billion a year.

The great majority of children are in care because parenting arrangements have broken down. Let us say that at least 50 per cent of this is the result of marital distress, partner chaos and related things. That will add £500 million to the sexual revolution bill.[25]

Health visitors and family therapists

Then we need to do the same exercise for health visitors, of which there are 15,000 according to the Health Visitors' Association, which is the equivalent of 12,500 full-time posts. This does not include a further 3,500 school nurses.

Let us leave school nurses out of it, and include one-twentieth of health visitor time taken up with supporting families through separation, divorce and related problems. That is the equivalent of 625 posts. Salaries average £17,500 before adding on pensions, national insurance and the administrative overheads, which means a total of around £25,000 per health visitor. The total health visitor bill is then £16 million – minimum.

We also need to include family therapists: specially trained counsellors who help families to 're-order' themselves. Such therapists are often called in when separation has occurred, to try to help family members make sense of their past and to find an appropriate way to continue life together. Let us say 50 multiplied by an average salary of £20,000 (again, the true figures are likely to be higher) – this means another £1 million.

Then there are child or teenage psychiatrists; there are 850 of them according to the Royal College. Let us say that the equivalent of 10 per cent of their time is taken up with problems linked directly or indirectly to parental conflicts and separation, step-parenting and other things. That will give us 85 employed more or less full time in helping children adjust to changes in their parents' situation. Psychiatrists attract fairly high earnings, to which must be added administration and hospital support. Let us say £50,000 minimum a year. That will add £4.2 million to the total bill. Nothing has been included here for in-patient care, which – as we have seen – is increasingly common.

Children with special needs
Then there are the costs of educating special-needs and 'statemented' children. While many are in need of special help to cope with education because of particular learning difficulties such as severe dyslexia, others need

help because of what has happened or is happening at home.

I used to work as a volunteer in a special school, and the staffing ratios in these schools has to be very high. The alternative is to place the children in ordinary schools, which can still be expensive. Some are so disturbed and disruptive to other children that some education authorities provide an extra full-time teacher for each statemented child. The cost of such integration then works out at up to £20,000 a year per child, including assessments, case conferences, family support, headteacher time and general staff training. (The cost may be somewhat less in a small specialist school.)

How many statemented children are there in the United Kingdom, and how many are statemented as a result of divorce or relationship distress? There are over half a million children in each school year. Let us say that 1 child in 2,000 between the ages of six and twelve has special needs mainly because of the traumas of separation, divorce, wars over custody and other things. Of those 3 million children in school, 1,500 extra children will be statemented. Let us say that the cost is only £5,000 per child; that will add £7 million to the indirect bill.

Care in the community

Now let us turn to the care of the sick and frail in the community. For a number of years I have worked with teams helping those ill and dying at home. From my experience, I can tell you that most people would prefer to die at home than in some anonymous hospital bed.

I can also tell you that however good the community care, most of those who live on their own will die in hospital. The reason is simple: in the last days and hours of life, people often need round-the-clock attention. Most elderly people on their own are widowed, but an increasing number are alone following divorce or separation.

Someone in the house is essential. Now to put a nurse or care assistant in day and night involves several of them doing long shifts, and this is very expensive. It is also very inefficient, because most of the time there is nothing for the care assistant or nurse to do. The person may be comfortable and asleep, yet still needs to have someone in the house. The nurse could easily care for more than one person – which is the way institutional care runs.

The ratio of care assistant to those ill is up to three to one at home – with shifts and cover for days off, holidays and sickness. On a hospital ward, it can be 1.5 to one or lower.

The reality is that most areas can provide 24-hour care, but only for a very limited time. There is usually great reliance on other family members at home to help. But in our increasingly fragmented society, how likely is that? Certainly less likely than it was. So what is the effect on community care?

Community care but no community

Care in the community is a major plank of public health policy in almost every developed nation, and many developing countries. This is because it is cheaper, with unpaid family members doing much of the work.

Let us suppose that out of the 650,000 who die each year, there are an extra 2 per cent or 13,000 who are seriously ill at home on their own, because single living has increased as a result of the sexual revolution. For each of these people, there is on average a significantly greater input of community services required. Let us add an extra £1,000 to the estimated bill for care, less than the cost of 24-hour support for two weeks, or six extra days in hospital. That will add £13 million to our total bill.

Relate and other advice

Finally, there is the cost of specialist organisations like

Relate, devoting time to supporting marriages or providing advice on relationships, housing or other things.

Relate's annual income was £9.8 million for 1992–3, running 130 local centres for marriage counselling. The Citizens' Advice Bureau in the United Kingdom has a huge network of information and advice centres in Britain. Their figures for 1992–3 show that 8.7 per cent of all enquiries were for family/personal reasons in 1992–3, but also 23 per cent for benefits advice, and 9 per cent for housing or property issues – all of which may be heavily weighted to those separating or divorced. There are many other smaller support, counselling or advisory services. I think it reasonable to take a total figure for Relate and all other help as around £15 million.

The other costs of family disintegration then stack up as follows:

Other costs of family disintegration (per year)

	£ (millions)
Social workers	22
Health visitors	16
Family therapists	1
Child psychiatrists	4
Children in care (contribution)	500
Statemented children (schools)	7
Community care cost increase	13
Relate/Citizens' Advice Bureaux	15
TOTAL	£578

Costing juvenile crime

Finally, we turn to perhaps the most contentious area of all: juvenile crime. We have seen there are many ways in which the sexual revolution is probably adding to the problem of youth crime, but the big question is by how much?

Let us first look at the total bill for theft, burglary and arson, and how much of this is committed by teenagers, before beginning to make a realistic estimate. The Association of British Insurers says that there were 384,000 claims for car theft in 1993, with pay-outs of £492 million.[26] Insurers also paid out £749 million for domestic burglaries,[27] and £325 million for arson attacks.[28] I have ignored thefts from commercial premises. Of course, insurance claims only represent part of the cost of crime, since many losses cannot be claimed, either because they are not covered by insurance or because of excesses or no-claims bonuses on policies. Vandalism in particular costs millions every year, but no official statistics are available.

Half of all crime carried out by 10–20-year-olds
How much of all crime is carried out by teenagers? Home Office figures for 541,000 known offenders in 1992 found guilty or cautioned show that one in five are aged 10–16, and a further one in four are 17–20.[29] That means that 45 per cent of all known offenders are aged 10–20, mostly males. One in three men have a criminal record by the age of 35.

Most offences committed by the young are against property. For example, 64 per cent of 10–13-year-old male offenders were involved in theft or handling stolen goods.[30] That means that more than 45 per cent of thefts and burglaries are committed by youth. Let us take a figure of half the total insured property crime bill of almost £1.6 billion, or £800 million a year.

Then we need to add a proportion of the total bill on justice and law: the £7.1 billion spent on policing, £3.6 billion on law courts, £1.7 billion on prisons, remand and borstals, £1 billion on legal aid, and £0.3 billion on probation costs, totalling just under £14 billion – not including the costs of running Parliament. This total is 6 per cent of government expenditure, up from 4 per cent in 1986.[31]

Let us take 45 per cent of that bill to represent the cost of running the justice and police system for crime committed by 10–20-year-olds. That will add £6.3 billion to £800 million.

Therefore youth crime now costs the nation at least £7 billion a year, almost 3 per cent of the entire government budget, equivalent to running up to 8,000 primary schools for 5 million pupils.

It may cost even more, because Home Office research shows that the younger people are when they first offend, the more likely it is that they will go on doing so as adults. Therefore, strictly speaking, we should say that whatever influences teenage crime is also having an effect on adult crime a few years later.

The bill for sexual chaos?

There are very few people who would say that there is absolutely no link at all in any teenagers between family trauma, unhappiness and delinquent behaviour, particularly after looking at the evidence in Chapter 7.

If you think that the effect is only 5 per cent, take the figure of £350 million. If it is 50 per cent, then take the figure of £3.5 billion. Let us suppose that only a fifth of the enormous cost of teenage crime is attributable in any way to family problems, and add just £1.4 billion to our bill for the costs of sexual freedom.

Total cost of the sexual revolution

The total annual cost of the old sexual revolution in simple economic terms is therefore already coming to almost £8 billion every year. However, there is another cost we have left out.

As we have seen, the British government calculates the

benefits bill for single parents as £3.4 billion in 1994; and we have already allowed for a lot of this in our calculations of separation and divorce costs. However, some of the £3.4 billion relates to teenage girls or women who become pregnant outside of a stable relationship, for whom there has been no divorce, or separation, or break-up of a live-in arrangement.

We have some indication of how common this is from the way in which births are registered. A total of 153,384 babies born outside marriage were registered in two names in 1991, evidence perhaps of an ongoing relationship at that time, while 54,000 were registered as having a single parent. Let us allow a third of the £3.4 billion for single parents who were not included in the relationship break-up calculations above. That will give a total of around £9 billion a year for the costs of the sexual revolution, equivalent to 3.3 per cent of the entire government budget in 1993.

Our total of the economic costs of the British sexual revolution per year stacks up as follows:

New total for the costs of the sexual revolution
(per year) (minimum)

	£ (millions)
Sickness and death/years lost	1,000
Divorce/separation/break-up	5,100
Family disintegration (other support)	600
Youth crime	1,400
Single parenting (proportion)	1,100
TOTAL	£9 billion

It is hard to visualise such a large sum. It is the same amount that is spent on all road building, road maintenance and railway investment. For the same amount you could pay for 26 per cent of the entire health service, or 28 per cent of all education in schools, colleges and universities – an expensive experiment.

Yet this is the *annual* cost. What about the cost over the previous ten-year period? It is not as much as the annual 1994 figure multiplied ten times. This is because we must assume that every year from 1986 to 1995 the costs were increasing until they reached that 1995 figure.

If the annual cost in 1995 was twice that in 1986, and the increase in percentage terms was constant every year, then the total ten-year bill works out at £67.5 billion, almost twice the entire annual spend on the health service. If the costs per year also doubled from 1976 to 1985, then the cost over the last 20 years could have been £100 billion.

On the same basis, the bill from 1966 to 1975 would have been £2.25 billion a year, or £16 billion for the decade (in today's money), and £8 billion from around the start of the sexual revolution in 1956 until 1965. That gives us the total cost of this disastrous social experiment as £124 billion in Britain alone since it began some forty years ago.

The next ten years?

And if nothing changes, then in the next decade, even assuming that trends slow down by 50 per cent until the year 2005, we will see costs of a further £110 billion from 1996 to 2005. Incidentally, the philosophy of the sexual revolution dictates there *should* be further growth. After all, no serious observer or participant could possibly look at today's society and culture and say that the new sexual revolution has fully arrived. So presumably, unless the old sexual revolution dies, there could be more of the same trends to come?

The British government seems to think so. For example, they reckon that the £3.4 billion bill for single parents in 1994 will rise in six years to over £5 billion by the year 2000. This figure is equivalent to a 47 per cent increase in six years, or 78 per cent over ten years if the same rate of linear growth continues.

So it is probably reasonable to reckon we should add £110 billion to our previous 40-year total of £124 billion to give us a 50-year cost of over £230 billion in sheer cash terms alone – almost as much as the entire government budget in 1994, and most of it spent in just 20 years.

Costs in the United States?

So what are the equivalent costs in other nations? US health care is even more expensive: the cost of a week in hospital is around $7,000, but income support may be more restricted.

The number of AIDS cases is vastly greater in the United States, and so is the percentage of single parents. Let us take a rough costing of $100,000 per AIDS case for the 50,000 or so people who die each year. The bill for AIDS care alone then stacks up to over $5 billion. Some of this is due to HIV from drug use or blood products, but it is more than offset by other incidental costs of HIV – including blood screening, and other anti-infection measures. If we keep a similar ratio for costs of years of economic life lost then the added costs will be a further $12.5 billion – making a total AIDS bill for the United States in excess of $17 billion a year (not including spending on prevention).

We also need to allow for treating STDs, cervical cancer screening and treatment, and infertility. We calculated this at around $200 million for the United Kingdom. Most would say that the cost of living, legal costs and the cost of professional advice are significantly greater in the United States than in the United Kingdom. A visit for cervical screening and examination is around $80. A family doctor consultation costs $32, and a visit to a specialist $150. Nursing care for an elderly person is $3,500 a month.

Let us say that all these and other costs average out at 50 per cent more than in the United Kingdom. I am certain this is an underestimate. We can then work out a minimum figure in dollars adjusted for the larger population of 255 million of the United States. That will give us $2.2 billion, in addition to the HIV/AIDS costs of $15 billion. We can do similar calculations for divorce, separation and break-up, and other support.

And the cost of youth crime related to the sexual revolution? If the amount of crime committed per thousand young people was the same in the United States as in Britain, and that the cost of each crime, policing and the legal process was also the same, we would land up with a bill for $10 billion a year.

Since the largest element of this is the salaries of attorneys, judges, police and others, most of whom are paid more than in Britain, it is reasonable to think that the US equivalent would be nearer $15 billion a year, even if the rates of crime were identical. So this is also likely to be an underestimate. We can do similar calculations for divorce/separation/family disintegration.

US costs of the sexual revolution (per year) (minimum)

	$ (billions)
Sickness and death/years lost	19
Divorce/separation/break-up	37
Family disintegration (other support)	4
Youth crime	15
Single-parenting contribution	8
TOTAL	$83

The total cost of the US sexual revolution then works out at an absolute minimum of around $80 billion each year. Working on the same basis as in the United Kingdom, doubling costs every ten years in today's money, then the cost per year in 1986 was £40 billion, and for the ten years from 1986 to 1995, around £600 billion. The total cost from 1956 to 1995 is $1,125 billion, from 1986 to 2005 it is £1,200 billion and the 50-year cost of the sexual revolution from 1956 to 2005 works out at $3,200 billion.

However, AIDS was hardly a problem at all prior to 1983, while we assumed a 50 per cent reduction of sexual health costs in each ten-year period, so let us mark down those costs. It won't make much difference because they are probably more than offset by underestimates in other calculations such as crime rates.

Costs in Australia?

The population of Australia is around 18 million, and the country has half the British number of AIDS cases. The costs might stack up as follows (in Australian dollars):

Australian costs of the sexual revolution
(per year) (minimum)

	$ (millions)
Sickness and death/years lost	750
Divorce/separation/break-up	3,500
Family disintegration (other support)	60
Youth crime	700
TOTAL	$5 billion

Note: Calculations based on a population that is a third that of the United Kingdom, and the exchange rate is $2 per £1. Youth crime rates/costs revised down further by 25 per cent, compared to the United Kingdom. Doubling costs over ten years – 1986 to 1995 costs are then $37 billion; from 1956 to 1995, $68 billion; and from 1996 to 2005, $62 billion, with a 50-year total of $130 billion. Costs do not include state benefits for single parents where there has been no split of a stable relationship.

Enough is enough

Enough is enough. The total global cost of the sexual revolution is impossible to justify or even imagine, yet these are cash costs alone – a tiny reflection on the sheer scale of human misery, tragedy, death and despair, robbing millions of life, comfort and happiness. The sexual revolution has failed to live up to its hopes: one frustrated generation, another broken, and what about the generation to come?

We cannot seriously contemplate more and more of the same, nor indeed staying at the same level of sexual chaos. Something has to give. It is unthinkable that sexual life and expectations will continue unchanged and the changes need to be profound.

But what will replace it? If we cannot go back, don't want to go forward and dislike the present, what do we do? Where can we go? The answers to these important questions will tax advertisers, social planners and government officials over the next decade. The answers will be provided not by people like you or I, but by our children.

So what sort of world are they likely to build? What are their options? And what can we do now as individuals, partnerships, families, communities, organisations and governments to help contain the vast medical, emotional, social and economic costs of sexual chaos in the meantime? These are the questions that we will examine in Chapters 9 and 10.

9

BRAVE NEW MILLENNIUM

We can learn a lot about tomorrow by listening to today's students. Ten or twenty years ago you would have heard and seen large protest movements – against apartheid, against war, for human rights. Today, those movements have largely died out, and students are more concerned with getting jobs. But what do they think about life and present-day values?

In Oxford, the Union debating chamber has seen many future Prime Ministers make their first speeches, and the policies of tomorrow's political parties echo around the chamber. One of the motions proposed in 1994 was as follows: 'This house believes in a return to traditional family values'. Such a motion would have been mocked derisively by the committee a decade earlier. Now, though, the idea of this motion was treated very seriously. Some 207 students turned up to give their own considered opinion as a gauge of our nation's future thinking. Ian Corby from Balliol delivered an inspiring speech about the need for loyalty, commitment and a sense of responsibility to children.

The result was that the majority of this sample of tomorrow's most influential intellectuals, those particularly likely (judging on past experience) eventually to dominate press, radio and television debate by the year 2020, voted to go back to traditional family values.[1]

'Back to Basics' – the slogan that would not fade
But what exactly were the students voting for? Were they

voting in favour of John Major's infamous 'Back to Basics'
crusade, which hit the headlines in 1993 because it struck
a chord with ordinary people, and made public fools out
of minister after minister as their own double standards
and sexual indiscretions were revealed?[2]

'Back to Basics' was a genie so powerful that not
even the media spin-doctors in Westminster could get
it back in the bottle.[3] *The Times* wrote: 'Tories may
be disillusioned with the Back to Basics slogan. But in
spite of all the setbacks they know it is almost impossible
to abandon the crusade.'[4] Within weeks, the slogan had
multiplied a hundredfold, twisting and turning with a life
all of its own. Supermarkets were selling 'Back to Basics'
foods – meaning they contained no additives. Insurance
salesmen were selling 'Back to Basics' policies – no extras,
no small print.

Politicians were writhing under the heat of the media
spotlight: it seemed that we wanted a nation where you
can trust leaders again, believe what they are saying is
the truth, and where people know right from wrong and
do the decent thing. But then came the scandals: bribes
for overseas deals, selling arms linked to overseas aid,
lies to Parliament, cover-ups and sexual indiscretion. Six
out of ten people said the Conservatives seemed 'very
sleazy and disreputable',[5] while eight out of ten said that
politicians were 'in no position to advise other people
about morals'.[6]

John Major said his crusade was not about personal
behaviour or morality, just decency and neighbourliness,[7]
despite strong moral statements about single parenting,[8]
and a new moral tone in sex education.[9] But still the 'Back
to Basics' slogan rolled on and on.

Voting for change

Those Oxford students were voting for change; they were

saying that the road ahead was a cul-de-sac. The end of the sexual revolution was in sight. It had cost far too much, and it was either dying or already dead. Many of those voting had personally felt the effects in their own lives, or the lives of their parents and friends. But what do we go back to – and if we reject going back, is there anywhere else to turn?

The new sexual culture that will come to dominate the next century will be a protest against the cost of sexual chaos in the previous 50 years. It will feel both radical and traditional – not a return to a previous age, but a new response to a new situation in a high-tech world. It will be an age dominated by mega-cities, mega-economies and mega-shortages. It is likely to be an age of upheaval, continued political change, of terrorism and civil wars.

It will be an age where it is a struggle to find personal identity and value; an age of mass media, mass travel, mass markets, mass movements, and an age hungry for micro-level living.

New values for a new age

We can speculate about the values that will be in and the values that will be out in the new sexual revolution. Here is a picture of the old and the new, deliberately painted in strong colours to show the contrast. We can see some of the new is already with us, while some of the old will linger for years to come. Every period of change has a large degree of overlap, because individuals and groups all have their own timing. So we will find people following both the old and the new for many years to come, with many somewhere in the middle.

'Me' becomes 'us'

Every age tends to be self-obsessed, as do individuals within it, but the late twentieth-century extremes of self-interest are looking tired and old: me, my world, my career, my sex life, my possessions, my happiness. The new values will be togetherness, team, our world, our future, our sex life, our possessions, our happiness.

The best things in life can't be bought
Likewise, every age has been materialistic – but ours has been more driven than most by a desire for possessions. The old values are wanting things that cost money; spending time earning as much as possible; sacrificing relationships for jobs; wanting a bigger house, a more expensive car; no commitment to a locality – perhaps just passing through on their way up the career/possessions ladder; high job mobility; sensation-seeking; one-night stands; short-term relationships; neglect of parents; the willingness to take bribes and backhanders, or conduct insider dealing.

The new values will be centred on the belief that many of the best things in life cannot be bought – personal happiness, contentment, love and affection – and many will try to have more free time (in exchange for less money) so that they can enjoy these things. Anti-consumerism will be common: 'greener' people who preserve the world's limited resources. A good relationship will be seen to be worth more than a better orgasm. Belonging to a community will be felt to be important: this will mean lower levels of geographical mobility and the commitment to living and working in one area.

New values will give greater attention to children and family, including grandparents. New values will insist on integrity from those in public life.

Personal meaning and spiritual experience
The ideas of right and wrong, better or worse, have been out of fashion, but are now being rediscovered. The result will be a rejection of a world without values or boundaries,

seen as a chaotic anarchy of individual views and feelings. Old values are pragmatic when it comes to morality – if it works for you, then it's fine by me. The old moral code is dominated by what is deemed 'politically correct' rather than standards of moral certainty.

The new values will be more intuitive, a search for personal meaning as well as for love, identity and significance; respecting passionate conviction and spirituality; seeing life itself as a mystery, and being hungry for spiritual experience.

Value of family

The phase that is now passing has been one where families, fathers – and men in general – have been heavily criticised, ridiculed and attacked. The old values include a rejection of a happy two-parent household as an ideal for young children to grow up in, a reliance on the state to replace the individual in terms of financial security, adult attention and the emotional development of children; fathers who are able to walk away from roles and responsibilities with approval.

Old values also include a devaluing of mother/child relationships, rejection of family history and older generational ties; rejection of parenting as a worthwhile full-time job; approval of paid substitute parents; dishonouring those who parent their own children without financial gain.

New values will include a growing recognition of the unique role that two parents have in creating an ideal climate in which babies and young children can flourish; recognition of the damage of separation and divorce on growing children. New values will reject state support as an adequate substitute for a missing parent, with disapproval of irresponsible men who risk pregnancy, but are unwilling to help a woman and their child live with the consequences.

New values will also include a new emphasis on unique

relationships between a mother and child, and a father and child; seeing family history and the older generation as vitally important to the richness and stability of family life; seeing parenting of young children as a full-time, important job; honouring those who sacrifice money to give children their best attention.

A new puritanism?

Almost every aspect of the new culture can be seen in some measure today, gradually growing in strength. The new ideas at first sight look very like the beginnings of a new puritanism, but is it? In the United States, a strong alliance of Christian groups has already become a growing force in sex-education policy; and more recently, this force was strong enough to influence the selection of Republican Party candidates in at least six states in 1994.

There is already a growing culture war between the old and the new, but support for the new is not confined only to those who go to church.

In the United Kingdom, the Movement for Christian Democracy became a new, rapidly growing, influential force in the early 1990s. Their newspaper quickly grew to an estimated readership of over 40,000 by 1994.

A campaigning group called Care was launched in the early 1980s, following on from a Christian 'Festival of Light' – essentially, a protest against a perceived moral collapse of the nation. The Care Trust now has a mailing list of over 80,000, and campaigns on a broad range of issues – including pornography and family life. One section of this large, rapidly growing and power-ful organisation is Care for the Family, and tens of thousands have attended their seminars on preserving marriage in the United Kingdom over the last three years alone.

The Listeners' and Viewers' Association, founded by

Mary Whitehouse in the 1970s, now has over 150,000 members.

These groups I have mentioned are large, drawing their support from many different people.

In the United States, 50,000 men recently attended a rally at a football stadium addressed by the influential Christian writer and broadcaster Dr James Dobson,[10] where they heard speeches on new models of the family and fatherhood. And on 25 June 1994, an estimated 1.5 million in the United States joined in over two hundred city marches as part of an annual event called 'March for Jesus'. They were joining in an act of Christian solidarity, standing up for values that they hope will become mainstream.

In Britain, the home of the March for Jesus movement, some 100,000 marched in four cities on 25 June 1994, while on the same day marches took place throughout the world in a total of 160 nations across every time zone, with up to 12 million taking part. Never has such a large number of people agreed to *do* the same thing and *say* the same thing at one particular time.

A spiritual awakening

Religious fundamentalism has been seen as a growing phenomenon in many countries – whether among Muslims, Christians or other groups. However, the March for Jesus movement is not so easy to label and dismiss, uniting millions of ordinary men and women from every church background and denomination in a common cry that enough is enough, and that something has to change.

Evangelical churches have always had a strong mandate for changing culture, and have much more in common with Roman Catholics than many suppose, when it comes to issues relating to ethics, lifestyle and social justice (as seen recently in debates over issues such as euthanasia or pornography). Evangelical churches worldwide are experiencing rapid growth, with at least one new person finding faith every second (1.5 million every month).[11] So rapid is the growth, particularly among Evangelical charismatics with their emphasis on enthusiastic, spiritual experience and the power of God, that an estimated 4.3 million new churches are likely to be established between 1991 and the year 2001. The percentage of Evangelicals in the world population has doubled over the last 24 years to 10 per cent.

It is hard to understand how this can be possible if you live in a country like the United Kingdom, where only one in ten go to church each week. This is because the rapid growth of Evangelical churches has largely been hidden by the continued collapse of mainstream denominational attendance. However 'revival' is already very obvious in almost every other part of the world, whether Latin America, Africa, the Far East, the former Eastern Bloc, or – to a lesser extent – North America, with early signs of positive future 'revival' in Britain following the so-called 'Toronto Blessing.'[12]

The emergence of a new, dynamic and rapidly growing Christianity is undoubtedly going to be an increasing global influence for change. However, even without it, the social and cultural conditions are now such that major changes in the early third millennium are inevitable.

The biggest clock on the wall

We don't know when the new sexual revolution will be fully in place. The biggest clock on the wall is not the hour, day, month or year, not even the decade counter, but the turning of the century, the life and energy of a new millennium. A new season is beginning, a new era, a new age, a new generation.

We can argue about whether it will take until 1999, 2010

or 2045, but we can see the change is near. In historical terms, the new millennium is just around the corner. The sooner the new sexual culture becomes mainstream rather than minority, the more likely it will turn out to be a relatively gradual adjustment of behaviour and attitudes, creating a more balanced, acceptable and healthy style of living.

Delayed change is likely to be more extreme

The more the new sexual revolution is resisted by those who fear it, the more violent the eventual culture shift will be, as the toll of human misery becomes ever more apparent by the day. An angry, sweeping reaction against sexual freedom may lead to an aggressive new puritanism, very intolerant and hostile to all who refuse to conform. I see traces of such things already in disturbing comments and speeches by a growing minority in the United States. Therefore the fears of extremism could lead directly to the very things many want to avoid.

Thus even those who say they want more of the old sexual revolution may need to embrace change rather more quickly than they think, facing up to the failure of the old revolution to deliver what it promised, admitting the relational pain and other problems it has caused and looking to find a better way.

Change seems to be under way already, so I do not expect a return to old-style oppressive moralism, prudery and double standards. Instead, I see a progressive introduction of new ideas about sex and relationships based on personal fulfilment, long-term loving relationships, and family identity. These are values that are independent of background or religious belief.

So, then, a new sexual revolution is dawning, with a growing recognition that the cost of life after sex has been huge, but no longer needs to be. Life in a sexual relationship, based on loving commitment in marriage, can be wonderfully fulfilling, enriching for both adults and their children, and can last as long as life itself.

We have seen how the end of this millennium is likely to prove a particularly significant watershed, and we have looked at the global spiritual awakening taking place in many parts of the world. In the meantime, though, what should governments and individuals be doing in the light of the current situation

TEN-POINT PLAN FOR GOVERNMENT – AND WHAT YOU CAN DO

There are simple, practical steps that can be taken today to save life and reduce trauma. What are they? How much will they cost? How will they help, and what should we do?

I want to look first at a ten-point plan for government, designed to soften the harsh effects of the sexual revolution and to encourage positive change. I then want to examine what individuals, employers and the media can do.

Ten-point plan for government

1 Stop fining faithful people
The first thing that governments should do is to make sure that people who are married are not 'fined' by the tax system, as they have been in Britain. Until recently, unmarried individuals buying a house together got £60,000 of mortgage allowable for full tax relief on interest, compared to only £30,000 for a couple.

Today, there are still slight positive financial state benefits in favour of single parenting in Britain and the United States, and the value of the British married couple allowance is being steadily eroded. I am not suggesting that further financial pressures be heaped on single-parent families, who, as we have seen, are often struggling to survive. All I am saying is that we need to look carefully at the whole tax and benefit system to make sure that stable double parenting is being encouraged.

Marriage needs redefining. It has sunk to become a minimally binding two-year contract. Not surprisingly, many cannot see the point of it. We need to recreate a definition of marriage as a long-term monogamous commitment, with a particular aim of providing a place of stability for conceiving and parenting children.

2 'Wedding anniversary presents'

A step beyond that would be to encourage marriage survival by giving a significant tax benefit, not for marriage itself, but in proportion to the length of marriage (which is far more important), with an additional benefit for a stable marriage with children at home. Thus a couple married for one year would get a small allowance, with an addition at five years, increasing in steps in ten-year intervals up to, say, 40 years of marriage.

Every marriage that survives saves the government a small fortune. We should be rewarding people for staying together, especially in the crucial years when people have young children. The current flat rate allowance on marriage is pointless when people can be married and divorced 10 times in 20 years, yet can enjoy the tax benefit almost continually throughout that time.

3 Minister for the family – with a budget

Governments should recognise the central importance of the family by creating a Minister for the Family, and a government department. The UK government has done this recently, but only by loading an additional title on an already overworked Cabinet Minister already responsible for the Health Service.

A new government department should monitor and advise on all aspects of government policy as they relate to family life. One budget item in such a minister's brief should be research into relationship choices and maintenance of partnerships, feeding the results into regional centres that offer relationship advice before marriage, preferably before engagement, as well as marriage guidance counselling.

4 Teach people how to love

The school syllabus should also contain education on how long-term relationships work, as a broader component of what is still quite narrow and mechanistic sex education. If we believe long-term relationship stability is important for child development, then we should provide education and training – just as we would for driving a car or any other activity affecting other people's lives.

It goes without saying that sex education, including information about AIDS and other sexually transmitted diseases, must continue to be a major priority, using community groups that have already pioneered successful work.

5 Reform of legal system with regard to human relationships

Governments need to look again urgently at the legal system with regard to human relationships, for law courts are not the best place to work such things out. Measures that encourage informal communication and reconciliation should be encouraged, and the perspectives of children should be clearly heard throughout.

By weakening the law on marriage so much, we have created in effect a type of one-year marriage contract, because a marriage can so very quickly be legally declared over. It is difficult nowadays to see what 'marriage' actually means from a legal viewpoint.

It should be made more difficult to get married, and more difficult to cease being married. The aim should be to encourage thought and care in those embarking on relationships, and to give them help. Compulsory pre-marriage counselling, costing perhaps £250 per couple, would be a far better investment than paying out large contributions towards the £20,000 average total costs of a divorce. There should also be a longer period required between the start of a marriage and beginning divorce proceedings, with compulsory arbitration. Marriage must be seen as more than a one- or two-year agreement to cohabit, or there will be yet another broken generation.

6 Higher-value child allowance taxed as income

The issue of government policy on single-parent families is extremely sensitive. On the one hand, in the light of the evidence we have seen of the price paid by children who are raised by just one adult, we might wish to ensure there are no tax benefits or service benefits to single parenting. On the other hand, we do not want to return to the stigmatising and rejection seen in previous decades, which will simply cause suffering and encourage a further rise in abortions. There are burdens enough for a child in a single-parent family to bear without piling any more on.

A higher-value child allowance taxed as income would sort out many problems, helping the most vulnerable families to survive, regardless of their parenting situations. It would give extra benefit to all households with children who are on lower incomes, withdrawing benefit from well-off households with children who currently receive untaxed child benefit at the same rate as everyone else. Such an approach would also help meet requests for help with child-care costs by single-parent mothers who wish to work. Some have suggested that mothers should be given vouchers or tax allowances that can only be

used to purchase child care. However, that will penalise
those mothers who would like to pay themselves the
same money to look after their own children at home.
A general child benefit provides extra income with no
strings attached, and is preferable to a voucher or tax
rebate scheme.

Means testing of child benefit is very easy to administer.
The number of children could be entered on the annual
tax return, and an appropriate addition of taxable income
calculated. That would allow benefit to continue to arrive
at post offices or in bank accounts on a weekly or monthly
basis. The other way of doing it would be to run it all from
the tax return, so that children become a tax benefit.
Then those not paying tax would receive the same in cash
through income support.

The recent suggestions of 'workfare' for single parents,
or similar measures to get such mothers into the job
market, are totally inappropriate if they are to be applied
to parents with children under school age. It is quite a different matter, perhaps, if a mother or father has just one
teenager living at home, than if they have three youngsters
under the age of seven. Paid employment may be possible
in one situation, but unwise in the other. At a time of
high unemployment, what is the point of pushing single
mothers to get jobs, and preventing others from working
who do not have such heavy parenting responsibilities? We
are then paying the wrong people to stay at home. Parents
at home are doing jobs too: working, quite literally, to
build the nation's future.

7 Campaign to promote adoption process

Government measures should be introduced to encourage
pregnant women to remain pregnant if they wish, rather
than having abortions, so that the babies they do not want
or cannot care for can be offered to couples desperate to
adopt. Tax incentives may be contentious, because they

might be seen as indirectly paying people to conceive and deliver babies for those others who want them. However, advertising campaigns could be used to help create a positive and responsible image of a woman who has an unwanted pregnancy, yet is deciding to let it continue so that a suitable couple desperate to adopt can do so.

8 Urgent review of policy on absent fathers

Policy on absent fathers needs urgent review. Few would fault the general principle that in a society that is seeking to provide women with equal status, to dump responsibilities for parenting on to women, and then almost bankrupt them at the same time by allowing the men to walk away without a second thought, seems madness.

It divides a nation into two groups: women who have had (sometimes as teenagers) to throw away two decades or more of freedom, and men with no ties, no responsibilities and a lot of time and disposable income. That can hardly be right or fair.

One of the biggest problems is the large numbers involved. If the number of single parents drawing benefit stayed low, it would be a cost that civilised society would gladly bear. However, numbers are already too large for a Treasury bank account to be able to keep pace with, without significant extra taxation or expenditure cuts elsewhere. If fathers do not help support their children, then every taxpaying adult in the country will have to pay out instead. Growing resentment could lead to a backlash against the single parents we are trying to protect.

The process of sorting out maintenance is complex and traumatic for both parties. Whatever new steps are introduced need to be done with great care and flexibility, allowing time for measures to settle down. The British Child Support Agency is in need of radical reform. It was highly unfortunate that the entire effort at first went into chasing fathers who were already paying some maintenance, forcing them merely to reimburse the state for income support. The only beneficiary for all the anguish and conflict was the Treasury.

9 Extension of age rating on pornographic material

Governments should also seek to regulate sales of pornographic magazines and other printed materials in the same way as the hire or sale of videos, helping to prevent access by the young. That would mean a degree of self-regulation by the magazine industry – with, for example, printed guideline symbols for 18, 15, 12 and PG. Serious breaches could then result in a fine.

10 Alcohol and drug-abuse programme expansion

Alcohol abuse is a major factor in many family problems, and governments should look carefully at ways to combat this growing problem. It is unfortunate that the price of beer and wine has fallen in real terms over the last two decades, encouraging over-consumption. Membership of the EC has made raising taxes on alcohol a controversial issue, and deregulation of licensing hours has also had a similar effect. Awareness campaigns, school education and more treatment centres are necessary.

In addition, there is a real shortage of rehabilitation centres for those addicted to drugs – an increasing problem affecting many families. The long-term results are excellent in well-run units.

Thus there are a wide variety of measures that governments can make, in line with the cultural sensitivities of each nation, to encourage sexual relationships that are physically and emotionally healthy – not only for the participants, but also for their children. These relationships will have a positive effect on society as a whole.

As we have seen, the costs of continuing with the current situation are immense, and the benefits of change are enormous. It will require great courage by governments to take decisive action, courage they are unlikely to have until prompted by escalating expenditure and public pressure.

Major changes in government policy are very likely in the early years of the next century, because parties without marriage and the family as items high on their agenda will risk not being elected.

Individual action – what you can do

1 Campaigning for change
As individuals, there are many things we can do – for example, lobbying government by writing letters to MPs, or by supporting organisations that are campaigning for such change.

2 Sexual health
We need to take sexual health very seriously. That means thinking very carefully before having sex with a new partner, and realising that not to be in a sexual relationship can be fulfilling and releasing.

If you have a history of risk, a short examination will detect some infections immediately – although an HIV test result may take longer. Following a decision in 1994, there are no longer any insurance complications with an HIV test in Britain, unless you test positive. You should be properly counselled first before deciding to go ahead with an HIV test; sex disease clinics should provide such a service.

Use of a condom will significantly reduce the risk of sexual diseases. However, the real answer to anxiety- free sex is for both partners either to have no history of possible exposure, or for both to have been confirmed by a doctor as free of sexually transmitted infections, especially HIV, and to remain faithful to each other.

3 Longer-term relationships

Individuals can seriously consider a long-term relationship – a realistic goal for any two people who want one. The great majority of those willing to pay the price with unselfish mutual interest and devotion should be able to experience happy stable partnerships with mutual commitment to work things out for the rest of their lives. In doing this, we are also creating a role model for others, especially our children.

4 Partner choice

Those considering a new partnership need to think carefully about partner choice – drawing on feedback from family and friends as well as books, seminars, workshops and professional advice. This will assist in reducing the number of 'relationship accidents' that occur because of short-term passions. Define your expectations before getting too deeply involved in a relationship.

5 Investing in the future

There are steps that all couples can take to help to ensure their future happiness. If you want to stay happily together, then the key is continuing to invest in the relationship – just as you did when you first got to know each other. Listen to each other, take each other seriously rather than for granted, and share the load together.

The four most important phrases in a happy marriage are: 'I love you', 'Thank you', 'I'm sorry' and 'I forgive you'. If just one of these four is missing in day-to-day life together, you can be certain the relationship will be in danger of weakening through lack of affirmation and open affection, taking the other for granted, being insensitive, proud and arrogant, and allowing resentment to fester until it becomes bitterness.

6 Parents' action plan

There are also steps that all parents can take to help their children. First, there is the importance of taking children seriously, and part of that is giving them 'quality time'. They are only young once – and before you realise it, they will have grown up. Time means money, so important decisions about a simpler lifestyle may need to be made. Involvement in the running of your local school is also important if you want to shape what children are taught.

7 Extending family

If we have family life that works, then we can share it with others. For example, by inviting a single-parent family to join in a family outing, offering hospitality to the widowed or divorced, or others on their own, or having children to stay for a night or two when their own families are under pressure for various reasons. There are also many single people who have not had children, or been in a sexual partnership, who appreciate being able to be part of an extended family.

Grandparents can also be a great resource if they are willing and able and parents are willing to let them, whether with young children or teenagers – and often teenagers get on better with grandparents than their own parents.

In an age of mobility, families can 'adopt' others nearby whose relatives are distant, and hope that people in other places will do the same for their own relatives. Where there is great tension with older parents, or where they live some distance away, people will often find it a delight to help support an elderly unrelated neighbour. Thus community links can help offset problems of distance and relationship.

8 *If breakdown seems close*

If your relationship has hit a rough patch, it is important to seek help early – while there is still the energy and motivation on both sides to work things out. When there are problems in the relationship, there is no need to hide them completely. Your children will have a far better model to follow in their own lives by seeing that it is possible for two people with different ideas and personalities to live together happily and work things out. If the relationship does fail to survive, they will have a greater understanding of why it all went wrong, and it will be easier to accept.

Do be sensitive to children's needs if a separation seems near or is taking place. Children have thoughts and feelings too, although they may be very reluctant to let them show. Do also remember that for many children, even with conflict at home, they would probably still prefer to live with both parents under one roof.

Employers

Employers can help by making it easier for parents to be parents, particularly by being creative with such things as job share schemes, paternity leave and child-care arrangements. It should be regarded as normal that all parents may need time off if a child is ill, depending of course on the severity and circumstances.

Those in the media

Those involved in the media can help by encouraging positive family role models, and programmes that help people make appropriate choices of partners when they are hoping for a long-term relationship. The media can also help people understand the basics for successful marriage.

The media can agree self-censorship for materials likely

to influence children or teenagers – not to prevent healthy awareness of sexuality or sex education, but to encourage a longer-term view of stable sexual relationships as physically healthy, emotionally satisfying, good for family life, and good for children of the future to grow up in.

The media can try to be more discerning in reporting results of second-rate sex surveys, before giving an exaggerated impression of sexual behaviour – especially to the young.

CONCLUSION

Throughout this book, we have seen how the pendulum of sexual relationships is swinging once again, this time from relaxation towards restraint, driven by a new generation who are counting the costs of a disastrous and traumatic social experiment.

A revolution in sexual relationships that promised us freedom has left many in chains, in a world destroyed by sexual chaos, tragedy, loneliness, emotional pain, violence and abuse.

We have seen that the revolution that first enticed us with short-term enjoyment has now fuelled a vast epidemic, with several million dead and 15 million others doomed to follow; tens of millions of others have chronic infections, cancers, serious long-term damage to health, and related problems of infertility.

The revolution that promised greater emotional fulfilment and equality has left many devastated by adultery, conflict, frustration, dissatisfaction, lawsuits, depression, despair, and the pressures of raising families on their own.

We have seen why this social experiment has been a disaster for a broken generation of children, many of whom are growing up scarred, and are now looking for something very different.

We have seen how the cost in simple economic terms alone is measured in tens of billions in just one country over one decade, and is now a significant part of government expenditure in many nations. Most of us have to pay for this in extra taxation.

Yet we are already seeing the signs of change. We cannot possibly welcome more of the same, yet have little desire to return to the previous age of a rigid, authoritarian moralism. There is now a new moralism powered by worried parents and hurt children; by a new romanticism and a search for love in an age of broken promises; by feminism, fearful of sexual power abuse; and by the widespread spiritual awakening occurring throughout the world. We have seen the early signs of a distinct third millennial culture beginning among the affluent and educated; it is both traditional and radical, encouraging long-term relationships and stable parenting, healthy sex and emotional security.

We have also seen that a number of practical steps need to be taken now by government and individuals to help save lives, prevent tragedy, restore marriages and protect children. In taking such action, we are helping moderate what could so easily become a disastrous swing to the opposite extreme.

NOTES

1 The Pendulum Swings Again

1 Michael Mason, *The Making of Victorian Sexuality* (OUP, 1994).
2 'A history of happy families?', *Guardian*, 11 January 1994.
3 John Carey, 'The age of consent', *The Sunday Times*, 17 April 1994, quoting Michael Mason's *The Making of Victorian Sexuality*, op. cit.
4 Central Statistical Office figures (1914, 1994); *Daily Telegraph*, 28 April 1994.
5 Keith Waterhouse, *City Lights, a Street Life* (Hodder & Stoughton, 1994).
6 Ibid.
7 (British National Survey of Sexual Attitudes and Lifestyles) Anne Johnson *et al.*, *Sexual Attitudes and Lifestyles* (Blackwell Scientific Publications, 1994).
8 'The old masters of sex', *Guardian*, 31 March 1994, reviewing William Masters's and Virginia Johnson's new book called *Heterosexuality* (HarperCollins, 1994).
9 'A history of happy families?', op. cit.
10 Russell Baker, 'A drive that takes the pleasure out of sin', *New York Times*, May 1994, reproduced in the *Guardian*, 12 May 1994.
11 'US National AIDS Behaviour Survey, Family Planning Perspectives', *Washington Post*, 9 November 1993.
12 'Society takes a liberal turn in the 1990s', *Independent*, 29 November 1993.
13 Pan, 'China: acceptability and effect of three kinds of sexual publication', *Archives of Sexual Behaviour*, 22(1), 1993, pp. 59–71.
14 William Rees-Mogg and James Dale Davidson, *The Great Reckoning* (Pan Books, 1994).
15 Dr William Masters, on launching his book *Heterosexuality*, op. cit., *Guardian*, 31 March 1994.
16 Susan Katz Miller, 'America still embarrassed by the condom', *New Scientist*, 15 January 1994.

17 Ibid.
18 'Primary class has explicit lesson in sex and adultery', *Daily Telegraph*, 23 March 1994.
19 'Mars bar lesson revives sex debate', *Guardian*, 24 March 1994.
20 'Primary class has explicit lesson in sex and adultery', op. cit.
21 'Parents win apology over sex act words', *Guardian*, 25 March 1994.
22 ACET (AIDS Care Education and Training).
23 'Patten seizes on school sex row in moral crusade' and '"Smutty" guide banned', *The Times*, 24 March 1994.
24 'Sex advisers back book that Minister banned', *Daily Telegraph*, 30 March 1994.
25 Penguin Books (June 1994).
26 '"Smutty" sex guide puts authority's work in jeopardy', *The Times*, 25 March 1994, and 'Work on sex education suspended', *The Times*, 18 April 1994.
27 'Condoms backed for girls aged 12', *The Times*, 26 April 1994.
28 Make Love Last, CARE, Freepost, London SW1P 3YZ. Figures from Care Offices, June 1994.
29 'Anti-AIDS class alarms parents', *The Times*, 8 February 1994.
30 Ibid.
31 Ibid.
32 Ibid.
33 'Olsen *et al.*, 'The effects of three abstinence sex education programs on student attitudes toward sexual activity', *Adolescence*, 26(103), 1991, pp. 631–41.
34 The Vietnam War killed 47,365 in battle (names inscribed on the Vietnam Memorial in Washington DC). See Chapter 3.
35 'Women who pledge to marry virgins', *Marie Claire*, May 1994.
36 Ibid.
37 'When they are bad they are horrid', *Independent*, 24 May 1994. Resource from Crack Crime, PO Box 999, UK.
38 (British National Survey of Sexual Attitudes and Lifestyles) Johnson *et al.*, *Sexual Attitudes and Lifestyles*, op. cit.
39 A. Kinsey *et al.*, *Sexual Behaviour in the Human Male* (Philadelphia, W.B. Saunders, 1948) and Kinsey *et al.*, *Sexual Behaviour in the Human Female* (Philadelphia, W.B. Saunders, 1953).
40 'The shrinking ten per cent', *Time*, 26 April 1993.
41 Kinsey *et al.*, *Sexual Behaviour in the Human Male*, op. cit.
42 Johnson *et al.*, *Sexual Attitudes and Lifestyles*, op. cit.
43 Ibid.
44 Ibid.
45 Ibid.
46 Ibid.
47 Headlines like 'Women only love me for my willy' or 'I charge £10,000 for sex', *More* magazine, 19 January–1 February 1994.

2 The Search for Love

1 Lenaz *et al.*, 'The viability of abstinence in an inner city adolescent population', *Connecticut Medicine*, 55(3), 1991, pp. 139–41.

2 Schamess, 'The search for love: unmarried adolescent mothers' views of, and relationship with, men', *Adolescence*, 28(110), 1993, pp. 425–38.

3 *UK Social Trends* (HMSO, 1994).

4 UK General Household Survey, in *Social Trends*, 24, 1994.

5 (British National Survey of Sexual Attitudes and Lifestyles) Anne Johnson *et al.*, *Sexual Attitudes and Lifestyles* (Blackwell Scientific Publications, 1994).

6 'Hollywood hype adds sizzling raunch to family values', *The Times*, 14 February 1994.

7 Ibid.

8 Annabel Heseltine, 'Do you take your passion neat?', *The Sunday Times*, 13 February 1994.

9 'The old masters of sex', *Guardian*, 31 March 1994.

10 Nick Daws, *How to Find Your Ideal Partner* (Imperia Books, 1994). (Advertisement in *The Times*, 4 May 1994.)

11 OPCS figures 1994; source Dateline.

12 Dateline literature 1994; also, conversations with staff.

13 'Six page recipe for a more successful marriage', *Independent*, 29 April 1994.

14 'Register Office ban on guide to wedded joy', *Sunday Telegraph*, 17 April 1994; and 'Read this leaflet, save your marriage', *Independent*, 18 April 1994.

15 'Changing values', *Guardian*, 11 January 1994.

16 'Society takes a liberal turn in the 1990s', *Independent*/NOP survey, published 29 November 1994 in the *Independent*.

17 John Watson, in *Chicago Tribune*, 6 March 1927.

18 Glick, 'Marriage, divorce and living arrangements', *Journal of Family Issues*, 5, 1984, pp. 7–26.

19 'Adultery a betrayal', *Daily Telegraph*, 4 January 1994 – Gallup survey of November 1993 polling 1,014 women aged between 18 and 65.

20 'Confused males are trying hard to please', *Daily Telegraph*, 7 January 1994. The figure was in fact 53 per cent.

21 'Adultery a betrayal', op. cit.

22 Jane Alexander, 'Built again virgins', *New Woman*, May 1994.

23 Ibid.

24 Desmond Morris, *The Naked Ape* (Vintage Books, revised edn 1994).

25 'Teenagers turn to friends and TV for sex education', *The Times*, 28 March 1994.

26 Vatten and Borve, 'Marital status and the first consultation at a psychiatric outpatient clinic. A five year follow-up study',

Tidsskrift for Den Norske Laegeforening (Norwegian Journal), 109(13), 1989, pp. 1395–8.

27 Ibid.

28 Baker, 'The spouse's positive effect on the stroke patient's recovery', *Rehabilitation Nursing*, 18(1), 1993, pp. 30–3.

29 Umberson, 'Gender, marital status and the social control of health behaviour', *Social Science and Medicine*, 34(8), 1992, pp. 907–17.

30 Ibid.

31 Ibid.

32 Wyke and Ford, 'Competing explanations for associations between marital status and health', *Social Science and Medicine*, 34(5), 1992, pp. 523–32.

33 Ibid.

34 Ganong and Coleman, 'Remarriage and health', *Nursing and Health*, 14(3), 1991, pp. 205–11.

35 Horwitz and White, 'Becoming married, depression and alcohol problems among young adults', *Journal of Health and Social Behaviour*, 32(3), 1991, pp. 221–37.

36 Andrew Roberts, 'Why the cult of youth is bad for politics', *Sunday Telegraph*, 22 May 1994. His book, *Eminent Churchillians*, is published by Weidenfeld and Nicolson, 1994.

37 Neugarten, in 1968, quoted by Maltas, 'Trouble in Paradise: marital crises of midlife', *Psychiatry*, 55(2), 1992, pp. 122–31.

38 Ibid.

39 Dr James Bevan, *Sex and Your Health* (Cedar, 1990).

40 'The old masters of sex', op. cit., on the publication of William Masters's and Virginia Johnson's *Heterosexuality* (Harper-Collins, 1994).

3 False Freedom

1 B.F. Skinner, *Science and Human Behavior* (New York, Free Press, 1965).

2 Mary Kenny, 'Unsafe sex, dangerous publicity', *Sunday Telegraph*, 13 February 1994. This concerned an MP who accidentally strangled himself, lying on a kitchen table with a flex round his neck, while trying to increase his enjoyment of sensations during masturbation. This is a highly dangerous practice.

3 Martin Mears, 'When sex is crime', *Sunday Telegraph*, 12 June 1994.

4 'Man cleared of raping wife two days after she said yes', *Daily Telegraph*, 30 March 1994.

5 'Vivisect la difference?', *The Sunday Times*, 30 January 1994.

6 Ibid.

7 'Expel pupils who lie about sex abuse, say teachers', *Daily Telegraph*, 7 April 1994.

8 Ibid.
9 Ibid.
10 *Oxford English Dictionary* (Oxford University Press).
11 Katie Roiphe, *The Morning After: Sex, Fear and Feminism* (Hamish Hamilton, 1994).
12 'Date rape: the story of an epidemic and those who deny it', *Ms* magazine, October 1985.
13 'A new recognition of the realities of Date Rape', *New York Times*, 23 October 1985.
14 Professor Neil Gilbert (University of California), 'Realities and mythologies of rape', *Society*, 29, May–June 1992.
15 'Who are the feminist gurus now?', *Sunday Telegraph*, 14 November 1993.
16 Ibid.
17 Naomi Wolf, *Fire with Fire* (Chatto & Windus, 1993) – also author of *The Beauty Myth* (Vintage Books, 1991); Roiphe, *The Morning After*, op. cit.
18 Roiphe, *The Morning After*, op. cit.
19 Catherine MacKinnon, *Feminism Unmodified* (Harvard University Press, 1987).
20 Shere Hite, *The Hite Report on the Family* (Bloomsbury, 1994). Quotes from 'Sons and lovers', *Guardian*, 3 March 1994.
21 David Thomas, 'Men: the season's best buys', *Sunday Telegraph*, 13 February 1994.
22 *Trenton Times*, 31 July 1992.
23 *Acquaintance Rape: Is Dating Dangerous?* (American College Health Association, Rockville, Maryland, 1991).
24 'Queen moves to check porn advance', *Independent*, 11 June 1994.
25 'Clinton sex accuser seeks support', *Independent*, May 1994.
26 Ibid.
27 Wolf, *Fire with Fire*, op. cit.; and Russell Baker, of the *New York Times*, 'A drive that takes the fun out of sin', reproduced in the *Guardian*, 12 May 1994.
28 'Sexual harassment', *Guardian*, 12 February 1993.
29 'Policewomen had experienced sexual harassment', *Guardian*, 12 February 1993.
30 Gallup poll: 'Confused males are trying hard to please', *Daily Telegraph*, 7 January 1994.
31 'Fire department pours cold water on sizzling centrefolds', *Independent*, 9 June 1994.
32 Catherine MacKinnon, *Only Words* (HarperCollins, 1994).
33 'All in a night's work' – Maggie O'Kane on the male escort business, *Guardian*, 21 March 1994.
34 Ibid.
35 Personal communication from a school in London, April 1994.

36 Personal communication.
37 Jackson, 'Pornography: clearing the shelves', *Health Visitor*, 63(3), 1990, p. 81.
38 'No nudes is good news as Rupe considers the big *Sun* cover-up', *Guardian*, front page, 25 February 1994.
39 Ibid.
40 *New Woman*, July 1992.
41 Presost, 'Influence of sex guilt on mood state following exposure to sexual stimuli', *Psychological Reports*, 73(1), 1993, pp. 201–2.
42 Nutter and Kearns, 'Patterns of exposure to sexually explicit material among sex offenders, child molesters and controls', *Journal of Sex and Marital Therapy*, 19(1), 1993, pp. 77–85. See Zillman and Bryant, 'Pornography: research advances and policy considerations', in D. Zillman and J. Byrant (eds), *Pornography: Recent Advances and Policy Considerations*, Lawrence Erlbaum, 1989.
43 Kutchinsky, 'Pornography and rape: theory and practice? Evidence from crime data in four countries where pornography is easily available', *International Journal of Law and Psychiatry*, 14(1–2), 1991, pp. 47–64.
44 Ibid.
45 Baron and Straus, 'Rape and its relation to social disorganisation, pornography, and inequality in the USA', *Medicine and Law*, 8(3), 1989, pp. 209–32.
46 'Cult video blamed over killing', *The Times*, 22 March 1994.
47 *The Interactive Lover's Guide*, PC Zone, 1994.
48 'Boy sex attacker "pushed over the edge" by computer porn', *Independent*, 3 March 1994.
49 'Boy, 13, attacked girl after watching porn on computer', *Daily Telegraph*, 3 March 1994.
50 'Censor's fears for video age children', *Daily Telegraph*, 8 April 1994.
51 'Howard in video ban retreat', *Guardian*, 13 April 1994; also, 'Alton's powers', *Sunday Telegraph*, 17 April 1994.
52 'New video labels will spell out sex and violence content', *The Times*, 17 May 1994.
53 'Video shops face under-age rentals curb', *Guardian*, 12 April 1994.
54 'MPs call for curbs on video porn', *Daily Telegraph*, 23 February 1994 – Home Affairs Committee, House of Commons.
55 'Chief censor says video will hit film classics', *Daily Telegraph*, 11 April 1994.
56 Personal communication from listener, January 1994.
57 'Young offenders' viewing habits "normal"', *Guardian*, 12 April 1994.

58 'Teachers claim video games damage children', *Independent*, 18 April 1994.
59 Ibid.
60 Ibid.
61 'Young Offenders and the Media', PSI report highlighted in the *Guardian*, 12 April 1994.
62 'Parents blame TV programme for son's wrecking spree', *The Times*, 7 April 1994.
63 'Censor's fears for video age children', op. cit.
64 'Why talk of penises, sadomasochism and erotic history of lingerie always ended in a row', *Guardian*, 18 February 1994.
65 'From now on we are going to cut more', *The Times*, 13 April 1994.
66 'Children of sex rings', *Child Welfare*, 69(3), 1990, pp. 195–207.
67 'Childish things for baby boomers', *Independent*, 11 June 1994.
68 'Exploitation redefined', *Focus on the Family Citizen*, 18 April 1994.
69 Ibid.
70 Deborah Holder, 'The naked truth', *Guardian*, 3 May 1994.
71 Libby Purves, 'The wrong sort of hugging', *The Times*, 7 March 1994.
72 Schamess, 'The search for love: unmarried adolescent mothers' views of, and relationship with, men', *Adolescence*, 28(110), 1993, pp. 425–38.
73 'What women most want at home is a reliable husband', *Daily Telegraph*, 4–6 January 1994.
74 Ibid.
75 Jake Niall, 'No more sex please, we're saturated', *Independent*, 6 September 1994.
76 Ibid.
77 Contributor to *Sex and Your Health*, edited by Dr James Bevan (Cedar, 1990).
78 *Social Trends*, 24, 1994.
79 *MORE!*, 19 January 1994.
80 Ibid.
81 Ibid.
82 Ibid.
83 Ibid.
84 *Just Seventeen*, 20 April 1994.
85 *Mizz*, 13 April 1994.
86 Ibid.
87 *BIG*, 20 April 1994.
88 *Just Seventeen*, op. cit.
89 *19* magazine, May 1994.
90 See p. 23–5.
91 *Just Seventeen*, op. cit.

92 'I was 15 when I had my baby; don't do it', *Independent*, 7 March 1994.
93 Schamess, 'The search for love', op. cit.
94 Dr Peter Dally, consultant psychiatrist, Westminster Hospital, writing in Bevan, *Sex and Your Health*, op. cit.
95 Margaret Driscoll, 'Left holding the baby', *The Sunday Times*, 15 May 1994.
96 Ibid.
97 Reported in the *Sunderland Echo*, 25 September 1993.
98 'Explicit adverts to cut teenage pregnancy', *Independent*, 3 March 1994.
99 'Sex was more fun when it was secret', *Independent*, 3 March 1994.
100 'Morning after pill set for general sale', *The Times*, 21 February 1994.
101 'Explicit adverts to cut teenage pregnancy', op. cit.
102 'Parents fail to give sex advice', *Daily Telegraph*, 28 March 1994, and 'Teenagers turn to friends and TV for sex education', *The Times*, 28 March 1994.

4 Sex and Sickness

1 Acquired Immune Deficiency Syndrome.
2 Work by Sir Howard Walter Florey and Ernst Boris Chain. Source: *Encyclopaedia Britannica*, 1979.
3 World Health Organisation figures, 1990.
4 Human Immunodeficiency Virus.
5 UK Communicative Disease Surveillance Centre, 3 January 1992.
6 Unless otherwise stated, figures here are from 'Sexually transmitted diseases in England and Wales: 1981–1990', *Communicable Disease Report*, 2(1), 1992.
7 Bytchenko, 'Communicable diseases of major public concern in the European region (estimate for 1989)', *World Congress of the International Society for Infectious Diseases* (Montreal, 1990).
8 World Health Organisation Expert Committee on Venereal Disease, sixth report, *Technical Report*, series 736 (Geneva, WHO, 1986).
9 *Pediatrics*, 80(4), 1987, pp. 561–4.
10 *New York Times*, 1 April 1993, and *International Herald Tribune*, 8 April 1993.
11 Dr James Bevan, *Sex and Your Health* (Cedar, 1990).
12 Ibid.
13 Leviticus 15: 1–3.
14 'Current surgical diagnosis and treatment', *Lange Medical* (1977).
15 Bevan, *Sex and Your Health*, op. cit.
16 'Current medical diagnosis and treatment', *Lange Medical* (1980).

17 Bevan, *Sex and Your Health*, op. cit.
18 Ibid.
19 Matthew Garrey and A.D.T. Govan, *Gynaecology Illustrated* (Churchill Livingstone, 2nd edn, 1979).
20 *Barcelona Symposium on Heterosexual Hepatitis B*, May 1990.
21 For further discussion, see Patrick Dixon, *The Truth about AIDS* (Kingsway Publications, 1994).
22 *AIDS Newsletter*, 7(12), 1992, p. 18.
23 *Journal of the American Medical Association*, 257(3), 1987, pp. 321–5.
24 For further discussion, see Dixon, *The Truth about AIDS*, op. cit.
25 Neville Hodgkinson, 'Aids in Africa a tragic myth', *The Sunday Times*, 21 March 1993; see also, the *Independent*, 14 May 1992, and *The Sunday Times*, 3 May and 17 May 1992.
26 Dixon, *The Truth about AIDS*, op. cit.
27 World Health Organisation figures, 1991.
28 World Health Organisation figures, 1993.
29 HIV infection: internal between infection and illness developing varies according to study and area – shortest in Africa, longest in developed nations. Many studies have suggested around 50 per cent with HIV developing AIDS in 10 years; 70 per cent in 14 years. What about the rest? Although longer-term survivors are relatively few, they are being intensively studied. Some have milder types of HIV; others have partial genetic resistance from HLA-BW4, for example. IXth International AIDS Conference in Berlin (June 1993).
30 Personal communications 1987–94, and HIV testing of large populations, World Health Organisation.
31 For a summary, see Dixon, *The Truth about AIDS*, op. cit.
32 Dondero and Curran, reporting in the *Lancet*, 343, 1994, pp. 989–90; see also the *Guardian*, 22 April 1994.
33 *New England Journal of Medicine*, 314, 1986, pp. 647–8.
34 UK government figures (CDSC) 1993 and 1994, and experience of AIDS organisations in London, e.g. ACET, hospitals, specialist clinics.
35 World Health Organisation figures, 1994.
36 *US Morbidity and Mortality Weekly Report*, 30, 1981, pp. 305–8.
37 '1960s African blood samples positive', *New Scientist*, 22 January 1987.
38 Few case reports since 1962, recognised as AIDS in 1980s, *Scandinavian Journal of Infectious Diseases*, 5, 1987, pp. 511–17; *Canadian Medical Association Journal*, 137(7), 1987, p. 637; 'AIDS diagnosis retrospectively in sailor, died 1959 (UK)', *Independent*, 6 July 1990.

39 *US Morbidity and Mortality Weekly Reports*, 1994. US population figure for 1992, *Social Trends* (HMSO, 1994).
40 UPI, 9 April 1993, quoting *US Morbidity and Mortality Weekly Report*, 1993.
41 'A monstrous monument', *Guardian*, 12 May 1994.
42 *International Herald Tribune*, 1 April 1994.
43 *Sunday Tribune*, 9 April 1993, quoting US Secretary of State for Health.
44 UPI, 9 April 1993, op. cit.
45 Official Uganda figures reported to World Health Organisation, 1994.
46 World Health Organisation figures, 1992.
47 Panos Institute, figures 1993: Alan Whitcside, 'The economic effect of AIDS in Southern Africa' (University of Natal, *Indicator*, October 1992).
48 Personal communications.
49 *AIDS*, 1(4), 1987, pp. 223–7 – 68 per cent in one area.
50 Personal communications from field workers.
51 *Guardian*, 8 August 1992 – quoting Dr Iswar Gilada.
52 United Nations figures, 1992.
53 David FitzSimons, 'HIV goes East', *AIDS Newsletter*, 9(5/6), 1994, p. 1.
54 Dr Michael Merson, Director World Health Organisation Global Programme on AIDS, *Toronto Star*, 1 February 1993.
55 Pregnancy failure rates vary from study to study. *Lancet*, 1, 1987, p. 323, puts it as high as up to 15 per cent per year.
56 Dixon, *The Truth about AIDS*, op. cit.
57 Public Health Reports, 106(6), 1991, pp. 602–3.
58 98,000 AIDS cases to be exact.
59 *Health for the Nation* (HMSO, 1993).
60 Further discussion, see Dixon, *The Truth about AIDS*, op. cit., Chapter 2.
61 World Health Organisation, 9 August 1993.
62 Also known as Retrovir, or Zidovudine, manufactured by Wellcome.
63 HIV resistance to AZT: *New England Journal of Medicine*, 320(9), 1989, pp. 594–5. Disappointing results of use in early infection (Concord trial): *Lancet*, 9 April 1994, pp. 871–5.
64 'Billions well-spent to stop us multiplying' – (editorial), *Independent*, 13 December 1993. For another view, see Matt Ridley, 'Food for thought if birth rate of the world trebles', *Sunday Telegraph*, 22 May 1994, quoting US National Academy of Sciences: 'The scarcity of exhaustible resources is at most a minor restraint on economic growth'. China is a country that takes population issues very seriously: 'One-child policy fails to cut boom in population', *Daily Telegraph*, 3 March 1994 – quoting *China Daily*.

65 HIV-1-0: see *Science*, 24 March 1994; also, the *Guardian*, *The Times*, *The Independent* and the *Telegraph*, 4 April 1994. For further discussion, see Dixon, *The Truth about AIDS*, op. cit.

66 *Newsweek*, 31 May 1993, and *China Post*, 26 April 1993.

67 2.2 AIDS cases/ 100,000 in UK, 8.7 Spain, 7.3 France. The 1992 figures, World Health Organisation/ Panos Institute 1993. Same trend for HIV; 30,000 in UK 1994 (CDSC figures).

68 *AIDS Bulletin*, 3:62, 1988.

69 *Independent on Sunday*, 9 May 1993.

70 World Health Organisation, *AIDS Surveillance in Europe*, 36, 1993.

71 *Lancet*, 338, 1993, pp. 645–9. Also the *European*, 7 February 1993 and the *Observer*, 21 February 1993.

72 E. Knox *et al.*, *Sexual Behaviour and AIDS in Britain* (HMSO, 1993).

73 *American Journal of Public Health*, 82(2), 1992, pp. 220–4.

74 Addicts have been more willing to use clean needles to reduce HIV transmission than use condoms during sexual activity.

75 D. Doyle *et al.*, *Oxford Textbook of Palliative Medicine* (OUP, 1993).

76 Also Ruth Sims and Veronica Moss, *Terminal Care for People with AIDS* (Edward Arnold, 1991).

77 Howard Libman and Robert A. Witzburg (eds), *HIV Infection*: *A Clinical Manual* (Boston, Little, Brown, 2nd edn 1993).

78 Robert Pratt, *AIDS – A Strategy for Nursing Care* (Edward Arnold, 1991).

79 Bevan, *Sex and Your Health*, op. cit.

80 *Health for the Nation*, op. cit.

81 Franco, 'Viral etiology of cervical cancer: a critique of the evidence', *Reviews of Infectious Diseases*, 13(6), 1991, pp. 1195–206.

82 *Health for the Nation*, op. cit.

83 Franco, 'Viral etiology of cervical cancer', op. cit. This refers to herpes simplex type 2.

84 Monsonego, 'Role of papillomaviruses in oncobiology of cancers of the cervix uteri and their precursors', *Presse Medicale*, Paris, 22(10), 1993, pp. 460–2.

85 Burger *et al.*, 'Cigarette smoking and the human papillomavirus in patients with reported cervical cytological abnormality', *British Medical Journal*, 306(6880), 1993, pp. 749–52.

86 Butterworth, 'Effect of folate on cervical cancer. Synergism among risk factors', *Annals of the New York Academy of Sciences*, 669, 1992, pp. 293–9.

87 Bosch *et al.*, 'Risk factors for cervical cancer in Columbia and Spain', *International Journal of Cancer*, 52(5), 1992, pp. 750–8.

88 Ibid.

89 Ibid.
90 Niruthisard *et al.*, 'Male sexual behaviour as a risk factor in cervical cancer', *Journal of the Medical Association of Thailand*, 74(11), 1991, pp. 507–12.
91 Ibid.
92 Bernt, 'Sterility – a woman's concern? Coping behaviour and partnership structure of sterile couples of various diagnostic groups', *Psychotherapie, Psychosomatik, Medizinische Psychologie*, 42(7), 1992, pp. 236–41.
93 *Infertility Information Pack*, Serono Laboratories (UK) Ltd, 1993.
94 Ibid.
95 Ibid.
96 Ibid.
97 Benazon *et al.*, 'Stress, sexual satisfaction and marital adjustment in infertile couples', *Journal of Sex and Marital Therapy*, 18(4), 1992, pp. 273–84.
98 Source: Serono Laboratories Ltd.
99 See Patrick Dixon, *The Genetic Revolution* (Kingsway Publications, 1993).
100 Foetus at 20 weeks' gestation has 5 million immature oocytes.
101 'Donated ovarian tissue in embryo research and assisted conception' – public consultation document, Human Fertilisation and Embryology Authority, 7 January 1994.
102 'Parents tell of joy over birth of "designer baby"', *The Times*, 16 March 1994 – after London Gender Clinic selects sex by separating sperm.
103 'Clone hype' and 'How will the clone feel?', *Newsweek*, 8 November 1993.
104 Personal communication with British embryologist. See Dixon, *The Genetic Revolution*, op. cit.
105 *So you want to have a baby – a patient's guide to infertility investigation and treatment*, Serono (UK) Ltd, 1992 – 33 per cent embryos survive freezing.
106 Amy and Elizabeth: second born 1987, 18 months later, same parents. Source: David Winter, *Choose Life* (Marshall Pickering, 1988).
107 Estimate by obstetricians in April 1993 at the Royal Society of Medicine.
108 Expressed during live television debate with me and three others, 1993. Similar comments reported in *Evening Standard*, 25 October 1993.
109 'Ethical split on cloning – debate raging over human embryos', *International Herald Tribune*, 27 October 1993.
110 'I was wrong, says surrogate mother', *The Times*, 4 March 1994.

111 Neugebauer *et al.*, 'Depressive symptoms in women in the six months after miscarriage', *American Journal of Obstetrics and Gynaecology*, 166(1), Pt (1), 1992, pp.104–9. Also, 'Psychological sequelae of miscarriage . . .', *British Journal of General Practice*, 42(356), 1992, pp. 94–6.

112 Roberts and Matthews, 'Unmarried motherhood', *Canadian Nurse*, 89(4), 1993, pp. 33–4.

113 Office of Population Censuses and Surveys, *Social Trends*, (HMSO, 1993).

5 Pain of Parting

1 John Adamson, 'The perils of womanhood', *Sunday Telegraph*, 15 May 1994.

2 Matrimonial and Family Proceedings Act 1984 – law passed on 12 October 1984.

3 *UK Social Trends* (HMSO, 1994).

4 Curry and Stone, 'Moving on: recovering from the death of a spouse', *Clinical Nurse Specialist*, 6(4), 1992, pp. 180–90.

5 Dr James Bevan, *Sex and Your Health* (Cedar, 1990).

6 Beckwith *et al.*, 'Identification of spouses at high risk during bereavement: a preliminary assessment of Parkes and Weiss risk index', *Hospital Journal*, 6(3), 1990, pp. 35–46.

7 *UK Social Trends*, op. cit.

8 'A slice of modern life', *Guardian*, 11 January 1994.

9 Ibid.

10 Ibid.

11 Office of Population Censuses and Surveys (UK), 1993.

12 'Society takes a liberal turn in the 1990s', *Independent*, 29 November 1993.

13 *UK Social Trends*, op. cit.

14 Duffy, 'Social networks and social support of recently divorced women', *Public Health Nursing*, 10(1), 1993, pp. 19–24.

15 Hall, 'Psychosociai predictors of maternal depressive symptoms, parenting attitudes and child behaviour in single parent families', *Nursing Research*, 40(4), 1991, pp. 214–20. See also Compass and Williams, 'Stress, coping, and adjustment in mothers and young adolescents in single-parent and two-parent families', *American Journal of Community Psychology*, 18(4), 1990, pp. 525–45.

16 Vatten and Borve, 'Marital status and the first consultation at a psychiatric outpatient clinic. A five year follow-up study', *Tidsskrift For Den Norske Laegeforening* (Norwegian) 109(13), 1989, pp. 1395–8.

17 'A single mother in an empty nest', 8 April 1994.

18 Ongoing research by Economic and Social Research Council, 'Failed marriages create a female underclass', 31 August 1993.

19 Cierpka *et al.*, '"Men only make dirt": a study of single mothers

in a mother–child program', *Praxi Der Kinderpsychologie Und Kinderpsychiatrie*, 41(5), 1992, p. 168.

20 Libby Purves, 'Sinking their clause into love', *The Times*, 25 April 1994.

21 Kobak and Hazan, 'Attachment in marriage: effects of security and accuracy of working models', *Journal of Personality and Social Psychology*, 60(6), 1991, pp. 861–9.

22 Ibid.

23 Malinski, 'The experience of laughing at oneself in older couples', *Nursing Science Quarterly*, 4(2), 1991, pp. 69–75.

24 Deal *et al.*, 'The importance of similarity in the marital relationship', *Family Process*, 31(4), 1992, pp. 369–82.

25 'What are happy families made of?' *The Times*, 15 April 1994.

26 Sutton, 'Do men grow to resemble their wives or vice versa?', *Journal of Biosocial Science*, 25(1), 1993, pp. 25–9.

27 Casey *et al.*, 'The role of work for wives of alcoholics', *American Journal of Drug and Alcohol Abuse*, 19(1), 1993, pp. 119–31.

28 'Having a baby can damage your marriage', *Independent*, 18 April 1994.

29 For example, Gottma *et al.*, 'Marital processes predictive of later dissolution: behaviour, physiology and health', *Journal of Personality and Social Psychology*, 63(2), 1992, pp. 221–33.

30 For example, Rodney Cate and Sally Lloyd, *Courtship* (Sage, 1992).

31 Ibid.

32 White, 'Determinants of divorce: a review of research in the eighties', *Journal of Marriage and the Family*, 52, 1990, pp. 904–12.

33 Booth *et al.*, 'The impact of parental divorce on courtship', *Journal of Marriage and Family Living*, 46, 1984, pp. 85–94.

34 Ibid.

35 Kitson *et al.*, 'Who divorces and why: a review', *Journal of Family Issues*, 6, 1985, pp. 255–93.

36 Booth *et al.*, 'Divorce and marital instability over the life course', *Journal of Family Issues*, 7, 1984, pp. 412–42.

37 Norton and Glick, 'Marital instability in America: past, present and future', in G. Levinger and Moles (eds), *Divorce and Separation: Context, Causes and Consequences* (New York, Basic Books, 1979).

38 Burgess and Wallin, *Engagement and Marriage* (New York, Lippincott, 1953). Also, Locke *et al.*, *Predicting Adjustment in Marriage* (Holt, Rinehart & Winston, 1951).

39 Lewis and Spanier, 'Theorising about the quality and stability of marriage', in Burr *et al.*, *Contemporary Theories about the Family* (New York, Free Press, 1979).

40 Huston *et al.*, 'Premarital precursors of the psychological infrastructure of marriage', in Gilmoure (ed.), *Theoretical Perspectives on Personal Relationships* (Lawrence Erlbaum, 1994).

41 Cate and Lloyd, *Courtship*, op. cit.

42 Ibid.

43 Ibid.

44 Burgess and Wallin, *Engagement and Marriage*, op. cit.

45 McCornak and Parks, 'What women know that men don't: sex differences in determining the truth behind deceptive messages', *Journal of Social and Personal Relationships*, 7, 1990, pp. 107–18.

46 Larsen and Olsen, 'Predicting marital satisfaction using PREPARE: a replication study', *Journal of Marital and Family Therapy*, 15, 1988, pp. 311–22.

47 Hill *et al.*, 'Break-ups before marriage: the end of 103 affairs', *Journal of Social Issues*, 32(1), 1976, pp. 147–68.

48 Tharp, 'Psychological patterning in marriage', *Psychological Bulletin*, 60, 1963, pp. 97–117.

49 Cate and Lloyd, *Courtship*, op. cit.

50 *UK Social Trends* (HMSO, 1994).

51 Whitley and Kachel, 'Altered parenting and the reconstituted family', *Journal of Child and Adolescent Psychiatric and Mental Health Nursing*, 4(2), 1991, pp. 72–7.

52 Johnson, 'Marital therapy: issues and challenges', *Journal of Psychiatry and Neuroscience*, 16(3), 1991, pp. 176–81. Survey of advances over ten years.

53 Relate national office information, 1994.

54 Gottman, 'The roles of conflict engagement, escalation, and avoidance in marital interaction: a longitudinal view of five types of couple', *Journal of Consulting and Clinical Psychology*, 61(1), 1993, pp. 6–15.

55 Markham *et al.*, 'Preventing marital distress through communication and conflict management training: a 4- and 5-year follow-up', *Journal of Consulting and Clinical Psychology*, 61(1), 1993, pp. 70–7.

56 Babcock *et al.*, 'Power and violence: the relation between communication patterns, power discrepancies and domestic violence', *Journal of Consulting and Clinical Psychology*, 61(1), 1993, pp. 40–50.

57 Hansen *et al.*, 'Therapists' perceptions of severity in cases of family violence', *Violence and Victims*, 6(3), 1991, pp. 225–35.

58 'Men: the best season's buys', *Sunday Telegraph*, 13 February 1994.

59 Rosenfield, 'The costs of sharing: wives' employment and husbands' mental health', *Journal of Health and Social Behaviour*, 33(3), 1992, pp. 213–25.

60 Fineberg and Walter, 'Transforming helplessness: an approach to the therapy of "stuck" couples', *Family Process*, 28(3), 1989, pp. 291–9.

61 Yoshioka *et al.*, 'Nagging and other drinking control efforts of spouses of uncooperative alcohol abusers: assessment and modification', *Journal of Substance Abuse*, 4(3), 1992, pp. 309–18.

62 Montgomery and Johnson, 'The stress of marriage to an alcoholic', *Journal of Psychosocial Nursing and Mental Health Services*, 30(10), 1992, pp. 12–16. Also, Schwarz and Wheeler, 'Dependency conflict, marital threat and alcohol consumption in a middle-aged sample', *Journal of Genetic Psychology*, 153(3), 1992, pp. 249–67.

63 Dawson *et al.*, 'Parental history of alcoholism and the probability of marriage', *Journal of Substance Abuse*, 4(2), 1992, pp. 117–29.

64 Maltas, 'Trouble in Paradise: marital crises of midlife', *Psychiatry*, 55(2), 1992, pp. 122–31.

65 Ibid.

66 Snyder *et al.*, 'Predicting couples' response to marital therapy: a comparison of short- and long-term predictors', *Journal of Consulting and Clinical Psychology*, 61(1), 1993, pp. 61–9.

67 Multiple sclerosis, for example. 'Multiple sclerosis: will it come between us? Sexual concerns of clients and their partners', *Journal of Neuroscience Nursing*, 24(4), 1992, pp. 190–3.

68 Labris and Lafond 'Sexuality and cardiopathies', *Canadian Nurse*, 87(6), 1991, pp. 34–5.

69 Shell, 'Sexuality for patients with gynaecological cancer', *Naacogs Clinical Issues in Perinatal and Women's Health Nursing*, 1(4), 1990, pp. 479–94.

70 Davies *et al.*, 'Till death us do part: intimacy and sexuality in the marriages of Alzheimer's patients', *Journal of Psychological Nursing and Mental Health Services*, 30(11), 1992, pp. 5–10.

71 Saarijarvi, 'A controlled study of couple therapy in chronic low back pain patients. Effects on marital satisfaction, psychological distress and health attitudes', *Journal of Psychosomatic Research*, 35(2–3), 1991, pp. 265–72.

72 Ibid.

73 Brown and Smith, 'Social influence, marriage, and the heart: cardiovascular consequences of interpersonal control in husbands and wives', *Health Psychology*, 11(2), 1992, pp. 88–96.

74 Arcel *et al.*, 'Suicide attempts among Greek and Danish women and the quality of their relationships with husbands or boyfriends', *Acta Psychiatrica Scandinavica*, 85(3), 1992, pp. 189–95.

75 Jacobsen *et al.*, 'Marital therapy as a treatment for depression', *Journal of Consulting and Clinical Psychology*, 59(4), 1991, pp. 547–57.

76 Bourgeois, 'Predictive validity of therapeutic alliance in group marital therapy', *Journal of Consulting and Clinical Psychology*, 58(5), 1990, pp. 608–13.

77 Starling and Martin, 'Improving marital relationships: strategies for the family physician', *Journal of the American Board of Family Practice*, 5(5), 1992, pp. 511–16.

78 Crowe and Jones, 'Sex therapy: the successes, the failures, the future', *British Journal of Hospital Medicine*, 48(8), 1992, pp. 474–9, 482.

79 Halhuber, 'Sex counselling of elderly patients', *Verhandlungen Der Deutschen Gesellschaft Fur Innere Medizin* (German), 97, 1991, pp. 369–73.

80 Apt and Hurlbert, 'The female sensation seeker and marital sexuality', *Journal of Sex and Maratal Therapy*, 18(4), 1992, pp. 315–24.

81 Faber *et al.*, 'Premature ejaculation – results of treatment of men of two different cultural backgrounds', *Ugeskrift For Laeger* (Denmark), 154(23), 1992, pp. 1638–41.

82 Crowe and Jones, 'Sex therapy: the successes, the failures, the future', op. cit.

83 'Behind the sex surveys', *Daily Telegraph*, 24 January 1994.

84 Montag, 'An empirical evaluation of behavioural and cognitive-behavioural group marital treatments with discordant couples', *Journal of Sex and Marital Therapy*, 18(4), 1992, pp. 255–72. Also Jacobsen, 'Behavioural versus insight-orientated marital therapy: labels can be misleading', *Journal of Consulting and Clinical Psychology*, 59(1), 1991, pp. 142–5. Also, Snyder *et al.*, 'Long-term effectiveness of behavioural versus insight-orientated marital therapy: a four-year follow up study', *Journal of Consulting and Clinical Psychology*, 59(1), 1991, pp. 138–41. Also, Baucom *et al.*, 'Supplementing behavioural marital therapy with cognitive restructuring and emotional expressiveness training: an outcome investigation', *Journal of Consulting and Clinical Psychology*, 58(5), 1990, pp. 636–45.

85 Jacobson and Addis, 'Research on couples and couple therapy: what do we know? Where are we going?', *Journal of Consulting and Clinical Psychology*, 61(1), 1993, pp. 85–93.

86 Voigt, 'Enriching the sexual experience of couples: the Asian traditions and sexual counselling', *Journal of Sex and Marital Therapy*, 17(3), 1991, pp. 214–19. Also, Lavee, 'Western and non-western human sexuality: implications for clinical practice', *Journal of Sex and Marital Therapy*, 17(3), 1991, pp. 203–13.

87 McCarthy, 'Treating sexual dysfunction associated with prior sexual trauma', *Journal of Sex and Marital Therapy*, 16(3), 1990, pp. 142–6.

88 'Relapse prevention strategies and techniques in sex therapy', *Journal of Marriage and Sex Therapy*, 19(2), 1993, pp. 142–6.
89 Ibid.
90 Metz and Weiss, 'A group therapy format for the simultaneous treatment of marital and sexual dysfunctions: a case illustration', *Journal of Sex and Marital Therapy*, 18(3), 1992, pp. 173–95.
91 Atwood and Dershowitz, 'Constructing a sex and marital therapy frame: ways to help couples deconstruct sexual problems', *Journal of Sex and Marital Therapy*, 18(3), 1992, pp. 196–218.
92 Russell, 'Sex and couples therapy: a method of treatment to enhance physical and emotional intimacy', *Journal of Sex and Marital Therapy*, 16(2), 1990 pp. 111–20.
93 McCabe and Delaney, 'An evaluation of therapeutic programs for the treatment of secondary inorgasmia in women', *Archives of Sexual Behaviour*, 21(1), 1992, pp. 69–89.
94 Flammang and Wilson, 'Marital therapy formats: an analysis of acceptability ratings with married spouses', *Journal of Sex and Marital Therapy*, 18(3), 1992, pp. 159–72.
95 Lazarus, 'When is couples therapy necessary and sufficient?', *Psychological Reports*, 70(3 Pt 1), 1992, pp. 787–90.

6 The Broken Generation

1 'An everyday story of rapists', *Sunday Telegraph*, 23 January 1994.
2 Office of Population Censuses and Surveys; Eurostat, 1994.
3 Bumpass and Sweet, 'Children's experience in single-parent families: implications of cohabitation and marital transitions', *Family Planning Perspectives*, 21(6), 1989, pp. 256–60.
4 *UK Social Trends* (HMSO, 1994).
5 'Society takes a liberal turn in the 1990s', *Independent*, 29 November 1993 – *Independent*/NOP poll.
6 Ibid.
7 Ibid.
8 British Social Attitudes Survey, 1986, *Social and Community Planning Research* (LandMarc, 1992).
9 'Adultery a betrayal', *Daily Telegraph*, 4 January 1994.
10 'How a generation of children has been broken', *The Times*, 9 February 1994.
11 Tripp and Cockett, 'Children living in re-ordered families', *Social Policy Findings No. 45* (Joseph Rowntree Foundation, 1994).
12 'Bad marriage is better than divorce for children', *Daily Telegraph*, 7 February 1994.
13 'Don't leave me this way', *The Sunday Times*, 13 February 1994.
14 Ibid.
15 'Bad marriage is better than divorce for children', op. cit. Also, 'Don't leave me this way', op. cit.

16 'Mental illness in children up 25 per cent in five years', *Independent*, 25 May 1994.
17 Ibid.
18 'Bad marriage is better than divorce for children', op. cit.
19 'Family break-up harms children more than rowing parents', *Independent*, 7 February 1994.
20 Ibid.
21 'How a generation of children has been broken', op. cit.
22 Ann Mitchell, *Children in the Middle: Living through Divorce* (Tavistock Publications, 1985).
23 Schamess, 'The search for love: unmarried adolescent mothers' views of, and relationship with, men', *Adolescence*, 28(110), 1993, pp. 425–38.
24 National Survey of Health and Development and National Child Development Survey, *Independent*, 15 September 1991.
25 Louie Burghes, *Lone Parents and Family Disruption*, Family Policy Studies Centre, published on 17 January 1994, *Independent* feature.
26 Ibid.
27 Ibid.
28 Ibid.
29 Rees *et al.*, *Young People Not in Education in South Glamorgan* (South Glamorgan Training and Enterprise Council, 1994).
30 '76,000 teenagers left without income', *Independent*, 1 June 1994.
31 Angela Lambert, 'Indulge the boss and spoil the child', *Independent*, 12 April 1994.
32 Penelope Leach, *Children First* (Michael Joseph, 1994).
33 Angela Lambert interview with Penelope Leach, 'Indulge the bosses and spoil the child', op. cit.
34 Anne Tiernan interviewed by Elizabeth Grice, *Daily Telegraph*, 6 January 1994.
35 Mary Anne Sieghart, 'How we betray children', *The Times*, 11 April 1994 – commenting on Penelope Leach's *Children First*.
36 Ibid.
37 Ibid.
38 Ibid.
39 'Male culture drives female managers out of office', *The Times*, 3 May 1994.
40 'Part-timers win job safeguards', *The Times*, 4 March 1994.
41 'More men do women's work as part-time trend takes hold', *The Times*, 16 February 1994.
42 Sieghart, 'How we betray children', op. cit.
43 *Independent* editorial, 15 October 1993.
44 'Working parents urged to rethink attitude to children', *Independent*, 15 October 1993.

45 Ibid.
46 Ibid.
47 Ibid.
48 Hall *et al.*, 'Psychosocial predictors of maternal depressive symptoms, parenting attitudes and child behaviour in single-parent families', *Nursing Research*, 40(4), 1991, pp. 214–20. Study of 225 mothers by University of Kentucky, Lexicon.
49 Zuravin, 'Severity of maternal depression and three types of mother-to-child aggression', *American Journal of Orthopsychiatry*, 59(3), 1989, pp. 377–89.
50 Gelles, 'Child abuse and violence in single-parent families: parent absence and economic deprivation', *American Journal of Orthopsychiatry*, 59(4), 1989, pp. 492–501.
51 Cox *et al.*, 'Marriage, adult adjustment and early parenting', *Child Development*, 60(5), 1989, pp. 1015–24.
52 Ibid.
53 'A monstrous moment', *Washington Post*, reproduced in the *Guardian*, 12 May 1994.
54 Ibid.
55 Daniels, 'Adolescent separation-individuation and family transitions', *Adolescence*, 25(97), 1990, pp. 105–16.
56 'Family stress blamed for 60 per cent of homeless young people', *Guardian*, 23 March 1994.
57 Ibid.
58 'Shock over runaways', *Daily Mail*, 8 December 1993.
59 'Number of empty homes hits 850,000', *Guardian*, 12 April 1994.
60 Browne, 'Family violence and homelessness: the relevance of trauma histories in the lives of homeless women', *American Journal of Orthopsychiatry*, 63(3), 1993, pp. 370–84.
61 Hausman and Hammen, 'Parenting in homeless families: the double crisis', *American Journal of Orthopsychiatry*, 63(3), pp. 358–69.
62 Dadds and McHugh, 'Social support and treatment outcome in behavioural family therapy for child conduct problems', *Journal of Consulting and Clinical Psychology*, 60(2), 1992, pp. 252–9.
63 Bayrakai and Kope, 'Dysfunction in the single-parent and only-child family', *Adolescence*, 25(97), 1990, pp. 1–7.
64 Simon, 'The single parent: power and the integrity of parenting', *American Journal of Psychoanalysis*, 50(2), 1990, pp. 187–98.
65 *General Household Survey* (HMSO, 1991).
66 N. Dennis and G. Erdos, *Families without Fatherhood* (Institute of Economic Affairs, 1993).
67 Ibid.
68 I. Kolvin *et al.*, *Continuities in Deprivation? The Newcastle 1000 Family Study* (Aldershot, Avebury, 1990).

7 Sexual Abuse and Other Crime

1   Susan Creighton, 'Child abuse trends in England and Wales 1988–1990 and an overview from 1973–1990' (National Society for the Prevention of Cruelty to Children, 1992).
2   UK Standing Medical Advisory Committee, *Youthwork*, June/ July 1992.
3   'Fall in theft may cut cost of insurance', *The Sunday Times*, 12 June 1994. Figures from the Association of British Insurers.
4   NSPCC report, op. cit.
5   NSPCC report, op. cit.
6   Home Office figures, 1994.
7   Home Office figures, 1992.
8   Home Office figures, *Criminal Statistics: England and Wales*, 1861, 1906, 1908, 1991.
9   Richard Harwood, 'A monstrous monument', writing in the *Washington Post*. Article reproduced in the *Guardian*, 12 May 1994.
10 Ibid.
11 Ibid.
12 Ibid.
13 Ibid.
14 Barbara Amiel, 'Bang, bang: why family values are shot to pieces', *The Sunday Times*, 23 January 1994.
15 Ibid.
16 'I walk the streets of New York at night but I never fear for my life like I do here in Manchester', *Guardian*, 11 February 1994.
17 Janet Daley, 'Why can't you behave?', *The Times*, 27 April 1994.
18 Professor David Farrington survey, *The Times*, 10 May 1994.
19 Ibid.
20 'Scots' crime rate falls for second year running', *Daily Telegraph*, 28 April 1994.
21 Rosie Waterhouse, 'Single mothers', *Independent on Sunday*, 14 November 1993.
22 Fethke, 'Life-cycle models of saving and the effect of the timing on divorce on retirement economic well-being', *Journal of Gerontology*, 44(3), 1989, pp. 121–8.
23 'Poor Deal', report by Barnardo's, reviewed in 'Estates' food shops top London prices', *Independent*, 31 May 1994.
24 Ibid.
25 'Study shows poor are dying younger', *Guardian*, 29 April 1994. *British Medical Journal* editorial, plus five reports.
26 House of Commons Scottish Affairs Committee report, published 9 May 1994.
27 Lempers and Clark-Lempers, 'Family economic stress, maternal

and paternal support and adolescent distress', *Journal of Adolescence*, 13(3), 1990, pp. 217–29.

28 Darling *et al.*, 'Single parents: interaction of parenting and sexual issues', *Journal of Sex and Marital Therapy*, 15(4), 1989, pp. 227–45.

29 Fergusson *et al.*, 'Family change, parental discord and early offending', *Journal of Child Psychology and Psychiatry and Allied Disciplines*, 33(6), 1992, pp. 1059–75.

30 Gartland and Day, 'Parental conflict and male adolescent problem behaviour', *Journal of Genetic Psychology*, 153(2), 1992, pp. 201–9.

8 The Cost to Society

1 Institute of Actuaries, 1994.

2 Estimates by Mr Peter Firth, gynaecologist in Brighton.

3 Royal College of Gynaecologists has some 1,050 Fellows in England, 75 in Wales, 120 in Scotland, and 40 in Northern Ireland. Estimates: Mr Peter Firth, gynaecologist in Brighton.

4 *Health for the Nation* (HMSO, 1993).

5 Estimate by Mr Peter Firth, consultant gynaecologist, Brighton.

6 Figure from Serono Laboratories Ltd, market leaders in the manufacture of infertility drugs.

7 Dr Andrew Fergusson, general secretary, Christian Medical Fellowship.

8 *Office of Population Censuses and Surveys* (HMSO, 1994).

9 Ibid.

10 Budget per school £700,000.

11 'Divorce mediation "reduces acrimony"', *Guardian*, 28 February 1994.

12 'Black hole of despair', *Guardian*, 17 May 1994.

13 Ibid.

14 UK 1993 figures: 'End of the "quickie" divorce proposed', *Independent*, 7 December 1993.

15 'Divorce mediation "reduces acrimony"', op. cit.

16 'Black hole of despair', op. cit.

17 Ibid.

18 'Single mothers', *Independent on Sunday*, 14 November 1993.

19 Ibid.

20 Ibid.

21 Legal cost average per divorce in 1993 estimated by UK government at £1,650.

22 *Social Trends* (HMSO, 1994).

23 *Social Trends* (HMSO, 1992).

24 Tim Yeo MP, parliamentary written reply March 1993. Of 55,000 in care in England, 32,000 were fostered (58.2 per cent).

25 UK costs from National Foster Care Association, 1994.

26 Association of British Insurers figures 1993.
27 Ibid.
28 Arson Protection Bureau (Fire Protection Association) figures 1993.
29 Home Office figures 1993.
30 Ibid.
31 Central Statistical Office figures for 1992: *Social Trends* (HMSO, 1994).

9 Brave New Millennium

1 Mary Kenny, 'Unsafe sex, dangerous publicity', *Sunday Telegraph*, 13 February 1994.
2 'Major defies critics over Back to Basics', *The Times*, 14 February 1994, front page headline.
3 'Back to Basics goes off limits', *The Times*, 15 February 1994.
4 'Major defies critics over Back to Basics', op. cit.
5 Ibid.
6 NOP/Independent survey, *Independent*, 29 November 1993.
7 'Nothing personal in Back to Basics crusade says PM', *Guardian*, 7 January 1994; also, 'Major says "basics" not a moral crusade', *The Times*, 7 January 1994.
8 'Major says "basics" not a moral crusade', op. cit. – quoting Michael Portillo on right and wrong, Michael Howard and John Patten on single parents, and a father's responsibilities.
9 'Patten seizes on school sex row in moral crusade', *The Times*, 24 March 1994.
10 'Focus on the Family' conference at Colorado Springs, United States. *Care* newsletter, February 1994.
11 Calculated on world population figures – percentage change in church membership. Figures from Operation World, 1994.
12 In 1994 several thousand UK churches were affected by a wave of enthusiastic, emotional faith, linked with physical manifestations such as falling down, laughter, shaking. Linked by some to similar experiences in Toronto, there are strong parallels with revivals in history. People from all walks of life have been affected. See P. Dixon, *Signs of Revival* (Kingsway Publications, 1994).

INDEX